Introduction

The book you are holding in your hands is an honest attempt by a surgeon who was in private practice in a small community for several decades to show what medical malpractice claims can do to the physician and his family. While the plaintiff's attorneys would like their clients to believe that it is the big insurance companies that they are after and not their doctors and while it is true that the brunt of the financial loss is for the insurance company, the multitudes of sufferings that the surgeon goes through often go unnoticed by the public.

All physicians, surgeons included, abide by the Hippocratic oath that they swore to at the beginning of their medical careers. The healing and welfare of the patient is always his/her ultimate aim. Long years of studies and mentoring and training did again reinforce this aim, and they will be the first to be sad and sorry when the perfect result does not happen at times.

Healing is a very complex process and multiple factors are in play in this complex process. I often think of the motto displayed on the large sign at the entrance to Tenwek Mission Hospital in Kenya. It reads, "We Treat: Jesus Heals."

Unfortunately, here in the United States of America, most people expect perfect results when it comes to healing in the hands of their doctors. When the barrage of advertisements by trial lawyers on the media is added, many patients are lured to sue their surgeons.

One major difference that I have noticed is the significantly shorter period of patient-physician relationship between the surgeon and his patients. In emergency situations like trauma, acute illnesses like appendicitis, gallbladder attacks, strangulated bowels, etc., the surgeon takes the patient to the operating room mostly immediately after their first encounter. Most of these patients will see the surgeon for a couple of office visits and there ends their relationship. Primary care physicians on the other hand get to have a long-standing relationship with their patients. It is a factor in the lower incidence of medical liability cases in the primary care field.

America is facing another medical liability crisis!

COVID-19 pandemic has affected every facet of life as we know it. Its effects on socioeconomic issues were global and widespread. Unemployment, underemployment, and increased stress on the job still continue.

The field of medicine still goes through stressful situations like never before. Both physicians and patients alike are still learning how to adjust to the new norm. Overnight, the new virus totally changed the way we practiced medicine. Hospitals all across the country became inaccessible to the public. Mortal fear of the virus kept patients with even emergency medical conditions away from hospitals until it was too late.

Doctors and ancillary medical staff were overworked and overstretched due to staff shortage and increased severity of the COVID-19 patients needing hospitalization. Even those patients who got hospitalized experienced extreme loneliness and stress due to the hospital policy of keeping visitors and bystanders off.

Overworked and tired health-care workers often had to pick and choose the patient who can get the more aggressive mode of treatment like ventilatory support.

Many succumbed to the severity of their illness and some probably to the staff shortage.

Most of the courts postponed taking civil cases and thus prolonged the waiting period for the plaintiffs in medical liability cases. Once the pandemic is over, the apparent low incidence in medical liability cases is going to reverse. The injury lawyers will come back with a vengeance, and there will be a lot more potential cases that they can dig up from this unusually stressful period in medicine during the pandemic.

Physicians, once served with alleged malpractice, are immediately placed under a *gag order* by their attorneys. They can't discuss the case or talk anything about it to anyone else until they *get their day* in the court. That, in most of the cases, will be several years. This will lead to depression and anger on the part of physicians and prolonged waiting and financial loss both to the physician as well as the plaintiff. The legal profession views these physicians as *conspirators of silence*.

Not so in other professions. Recently I was astounded to watch a prominent movie star under investigation being interviewed on national TV about his side of the story in the death of a staff member at the time of shooting the movie. This kind of privilege does not exist for surgeons and that has to change.

Painting the surgeon in an adversarial role in these cases is not fair. Not all unexpected outcomes are the result of medical malpractice. In the present setup, the plaintiff's attorney somehow makes any and all imperfect outcome the result of negligence or willful disregard on the part of the surgeon.

There should be a way to reform this situation. All the less-than-optimal outcomes need to be addressed as soon as they occur, and patients should be involved in the resolution of these in an amicable way. If the surgeon was found to be at fault, the patient still has the option to take the case to the court of law.

If due to failure of the system, like malfunctioning equipment or untoward effect of a medication, they need to be addressed ASAP instead of the system continuing to do harm for many more before the case is resolved in the court many years later.

Early recognition and remedying of the harm done to a patient, regardless of who happened to be at fault, will go a long way in reestablishing the sacred patient-physician relationship as well as public trust in the medical community.

I lost my hope in any legislative initiation to bring the incidence of liability claims down, as the majority of the legislators are trial lawyers!

Maybe newer ideas coming up from the grassroots level will bring an answer.

If *Surgeon on Trial* initiates a move to address the liability crisis, my purpose for writing this is served.

I am grateful to you, my reader, for spending your valuable time on this book.

Prevenient Grace

I knew you before I formed you in your mother's womb.
—Jeremiah 1:5 NLT

"I just came to see you and talk to you. Don't touch me; I haven't yet gone to Jesus." With these words, her son who was buried three days back stood at her bedside. "I am sorry they did not let you see me or talk to me after I got bitten by the snake."

With these words, he smiled at his mom and turned around and departed. As she tried to turn on her bed, she felt the newborn baby boy sleeping by her side. *Is this baby going to replace the one I just lost?* The loud bark of her dog woke her up from her dream, but that vision stayed so clear in her mind till her death.

Unnikunju was her twelve-year-old son, loved and adored by his mom and admired by all who knew him. He had a brother four years younger and a sister three years older than him. His youngest sister was seven years younger than him. One summer day, he came back from school, had a snack, and ran out of the house to play. His favorite playmate, the black calf, was ready for him to be chased around the yard. Seeing him running after, the calf ran down the sloppy yard. Unnikunju followed him as fast as he could. Little did he know when he jumped down the slope that he was landing on an extremely venomous cobra. It doesn't take much for the cobra to retaliate when provoked. He hit the enemy hard with his fang, injecting a lethal dose of venom into his system. With a scream that was heard all around the neighborhood, Unnikunju ran back home and collapsed.

Snakebite is not an uncommon incident in that part of the country. Most adults knew what to do. Using a piece of clothing, a tourniquet is tied on the limb above the bite mark. The victim is not allowed to walk; he will be carried by men to the nearest native physician—Vizhahaari—who will prescribe the treatment. Prognosis depends on many factors, including the time of bite, the position of the stars, and the birth star of the victim.

Once bitten by a snake, women should not see or touch the victim; even the mother is forbidden to see her child who is to be carried away for treatment. Vizhahaari has the antidote for various kinds of poisonous snakes, some to be given by mouth, some for application around the bitten area, and some to be applied on the head. Along with that, there may be a session of *dhaara* when cold water will be poured continuously over the head of the victim who is seated on a large platter. A few will survive, a good number will die of respiratory arrest, and a good number will start bleeding from all orifices and die.

A few who survive will have extensive nonhealing ulcers over the site of envenomation (depends on the type of venom—neurotoxic, hemolytic, or local sloughing—and of course the quantity of envenomation too). Unnikunju did not stay alive to see the daybreak. His mom did not get a chance to see her son alive.

Funeral arrangements were made in a hurry. No embalming, no funeral home, and no facility for cold storage. All friends and family were at close range. Messengers were sent to all relatives. They assembled at our home to mourn and console. The funeral was over before the evening. For Mom, it is never going to be the same again. No mom should bury her son/daughter.

Time has its own way of dealing with situations. Grieving is a long process, and there is no shortcut. A loving and supportive family, caring and praying community, and friends go a long way in alleviating the intensity of grief.

My birth on a Sunday morning on the last day of the year 1944 was the fulfillment of my mother's dream. That was the best thing to happen for Mom. She was already forty, but the baby boy made her feel and act like she was in her twenties! Until her death, she firmly believed that I was that baby boy by her side in that dream.

I, too, believe that God had called me even before I was formed in my mother's womb as He called Jeremiah in the verse in reference. John Wesley, the founder of the Methodist movement, called it prevenient grace. It is that grace that was there even before we knew it!

Looking Back to the Village Life and My Early Years

India was ruled by the British for over two centuries, and I was born at the summit of its struggle for independence. My first two and a half years of childhood were under British rule, and the long-awaited independence came on August 15, 1947. Second World War also ended around my birth. Many Indians fought with the British Army in World War II.

Division of India into Hindustan (India) and Pakistan based merely on Hindu/Muslim majority resulted in bloodshed and massive casualty. The total loss of life in this struggle was a lot more than the total life lost during the entire independence struggle. Two regions of Muslim concentration were partitioned off to Pakistan—the larger region on the west (present Pakistan) and the smaller but heavily populated East Pakistan (present Bangladesh).

Young independent India was struggling through several facets of development and planning. World war and the cutting off of food grain import from neighboring Burma had produced a severe shortage of rice in the state of Travancore. Through ordinances from the government, farmers had to sell all the rice they produced directly to the government authorities at the price they set. Cassava, aka tapioca, aka yuca, the starchy vegetable root that used to be poor man's food, came to the rescue of people in my state. Limited amounts of rice and kerosene oil were rationed for the public through the special shops all across the country. Unemployment and shortage of money were rampant.

By January 1950, India became a new republic. Negotiations with the many local *rajas* and some *maharajas* to relinquish their power and to join the republic was a Herculean job and the leadership of the Indian National Congress, especially that of Sardar Vallabhbhai Patel, is worth mentioning here.

The state of Travancore was ruled by a very popular *maharaja*, and he, too, gave up his crown and accepted the pension plan that was offered as the settlement. Even now, the people of Travancore show their love and respect to the family of their *maharaja*. It is worth mentioning that these kings were accepted by the public as representatives of their deity, Sree Padmanabhan. The enormous amount of gold and precious stones belonging to the maharaja were stored in the treasuries in the famous Sree Padmanabhaswamy Temple in Thiruvananthapuram, the capital city of Travancore.

Recently, a couple of these treasuries were opened, and the enormity of the treasures was amazing. No decision has yet been made as to the future plans for these treasures, and the enormity of the treasures in the unopened chambers still remains a mystery.

My grade school, middle school, and high school were at walking distance from home; and walking to and fro every day gave me time to develop lasting friendships as well as get necessary physical exercise. There was no stranger in our village, and it took the whole village to raise a child. We paid due respect to our teachers and elders in the community. Any mischief that a young person committed at school or on the way to/from school did invariably reach the ears of his parents sooner than later.

Looking back on those early years of my schooling, I recall those friendships that we developed between youngsters who came from totally varying backgrounds. I had good friends from varying social, economic, and religious backgrounds. Exposure to these kinds of friends with diverging backgrounds gave me an opportunity to learn a lot about the various castes and religions in our village and to experience the deep harmony that we had in our day-to-day life.

It is not uncommon to see a church, a temple, and a mosque built so close to each other and everyone respecting the freedom and right of the other person to practice his religion. It is worth noting here that a Jewish community had settled in our state as early as the late eighteenth century. The Jewish synagogue in Mattancherry is still in operation as a place of worship and a tourist attraction.

College Bound at the Age of Sixteen

Graduating from high school was not a big deal. There was no graduation ceremony, no valedictorian, no salutatorian, and no graduation gift. After the final examination, you just wait for the result to be published in the local daily newspaper. After a few days, you will be able to get your SSLC book from your school (Secondary School Leaving Certificate) and start with the search for admission for higher studies.

I had no reason to believe that I would be going to any other college than the one under eight miles from my home where I could easily commute daily from home. I still do not know why my father asked me to get an application for admission from St. Berchmans College, Changanassery also as I was on my way to the college nearest to our home. I was admitted to the college at Changanassery, and I had to stay in the dormitory. At the young age of sixteen, I left home.

For the initial few weeks, I was like the fish out of water. Slowly I got used to life in the city and life among the rich and the sophisticated. By this time, my oldest sister was working as a nurse at the Aramco Hospital in Saudi Arabia. She used to write to me on a regular basis, giving me pieces of advice in keeping my grades up and my life disciplined. I learned good study habits from the disciplined life at St. Joseph's Hostel under the Catholic priest Kuriakose Ernekkattu.

It was here that I met the premedical students and developed an interest in pursuing medical studies. At the end of the pre-university course, I applied for admission to the Government Medical College. Though it was very competitive, by God's grace I got selected and was allotted to the premedical class at St. Berchmans the following year.

I could have been posted to any of the three medical colleges, but I was sent to Trivandrum Medical College.

Influence of a Sister

There was a twelve-year age difference between me and my oldest sister.

My earliest memories of her were her carrying me around after she finished her schoolwork and other chores at home. She attended high school over two miles from home and walked all the way. Had to cross the Manimala River by ferry boat, as there was no bridge there at that time. Packed her lunch and took it with her every morning.

How can I forget the time when I threw a temper tantrum for my sister to let me have some sweets before it was served to some special guests at home? My sister lifted me up and carried me away to our neighboring property, all the while I kept on beating her up and she kept on promising me tender coconut juice and other goodies if I calm down. She was so patient with this brat!

After she graduated from high school, she decided to go to nursing school. She got admission to a nursing school in Vishakhpatnam in Andhra Pradesh, S. India. During her time in nursing school, she would come home for her annual vacation, and I used to look forward to her coming home always with some goodies for me. She was the first one to introduce me to the smell of the hospital by bringing home a first aid kit, used suture removal scissors, syringes, hypodermic needles, and the like. Methyl alcohol, tincture benzoin, and adhesive tape were all new to me. At times, she even had some procaine penicillin or vitamin B complex injections for us. Glass syringes and needles were sterilized by boiling in water before using them on us at home or anyone in the neighborhood. One time I used the tincture benzoin to clean the brush burn on my thigh and screamed my lung out at its intense burning sensation that gave me!

After her graduation from nursing school, she returned to Kerala and waited for a job. She took advantage of a couple of short-term job opportunities at mission hospitals in Kerala. Then she got a job at TB Sanatorium in Madras State. This was the time when nurses were in high demand in the Middle East. Aramco in Saudi Arabia was recruiting nurses, and she got an appointment there. Having someone in *Persia* was a big deal for lower-middle-class families like ours.

I was already in my senior year in high school when she left for Saudi Arabia. I missed her so much and was looking forward to the airmail letters that came on a regular basis without fail. She wrote all about her life in the Aramco complex—a Western culture within the highly restrictive and religious Saudi Arabia.

She was assigned to the operating room and soon became the favorite scrub nurse in the theater. I was fascinated by her description of scrubbing for surgery and staying sterile throughout the case, the whole time anticipating the next move of the surgeon and being ready with the particular instrument that is needed. The wonder of anesthesia and the magic of clamping and tying blood vessels before the patient bleeds to death all continued to raise curiosity and amazement in me. The mystery of healing of the body after injury or surgery always stayed a mystery to me! She kept her American surgeon at a high pedestal and considered his wonder-working hands a gift from the Almighty!

Did she ever know that she was instilling a desire in the heart of her youngest sibling to become a surgeon?

While in Saudi Arabia, she got a chance to tour the Holy Land. Every day while touring the places of biblical importance, she wrote it in her journal, and I got a series of letters from her, giving me an eyewitness account of the Holy Land. She wrote about those two-thousand-year-old olive trees in the garden of Gethsemane, the place where Jesus prayed in agony prior to his capture and crucifixion on that first Maundy Thursday night. From her letter, I could visualize the garden tomb with the large stone from the door rolled away on the first Easter morning. Lazarus's tomb and the Sea of Galilee were all described in detail. She wrote about the stations of the cross, King

David's tomb, and the Church of the Nativity. As a gift for me from the Holy Land, she brought a thin gold necklace with a cross pendant. I have been wearing that same chain around my neck ever since 1962!

Unknowingly did her letters spark an interest in my heart to make a Holy Land trip in 2007. While enjoying the scenes in the Holy Land, several times I thought about my sister. What an experience to trace the steps that my Lord walked on this earth! What a joy to feel that my sister is with Him now as I walk on those holy places! We had a wonderful experience touring through Israel and Jordan in ten days.

I left home for life in the dorm as I started with my college life when I just turned sixteen. My sister kept on writing to me on a regular basis. They were words of encouragement and advice. She often reminded me not to forget where we came from, especially as the majority of my friends in the dorm came from very rich families. She kept on encouraging me to study hard, pray, and attend church regularly.

She was so elated and proud when I got admission to medical college. Her prayers and support kept me going through life in medical college without much of a problem.

After her three years of assignment in Saudi Arabia, she decided to return to India and settle down.

Trivandrum Government Medical College

This was the first medical school in the state of Kerala and was opened in 1955. I was admitted to the class of 1963. This beautiful campus with the largest referral and teaching hospital, office buildings, classrooms, auditoriums, laboratories, facilities for various track-and-field sports and games, and manicured gardens and greenery all across is the envy of the two other colleges that were started at a later date. My home was a lot closer to Kottayam than to Trivandrum, and I was expecting my assignment to that medical college. God had other plans.

We were 185 in the class of 1963 at Trivandrum Medical College. Life in the hostel was good. Classes in anatomy, physiology, and biochemistry were tough. There were sources of distraction all around. Fortunately for me, finding a small group of seniors at the men's hostel as mentors did a lot of good. The value of small prayer groups as well as smaller groups of friends for sharing, caring, and being mutually accountable cannot be overemphasized.

Starting with the clinical side of medical training is a huge step. Going to the hospital in white coats with a stethoscope around the neck and dealing with patients elevates you to another level. It is during these initial years of clinical training that one learns the importance of intense listening, sharp observation, and using all the senses in processing the problems one encounters from each patient/situation. We were blessed with several senior physicians among the teaching staff as great models and mentors to emulate and follow.

Life in the men's hostel was good. I had a good number of friends for support and fun. We managed our own dining hall and the menu. Taking charge as the secretary for several months in that post gave me the experience in and exposure to managing the dietary department for a large group of *hungry* men.

Christian Medical Fellowship was an offshoot from our weekly prayer group in Trivandrum Medical College. The first summer conference of CMF was arranged in 1964. Groups from Kottayam and Calicut medical colleges joined, and we had guest speakers and leaders from Christian Medical College, Vellore as well as missionary doctors from elsewhere. It was in one of these long weekend retreats and spiritual renewals that Dr. Tharian from the mission hospital was the leader for our small discussion group. He advised us on the need for praying daily for our prospective partner in life. And I started doing it without a clue as to whom God is going to bring to my life. Little did I know then that my soul mate was attending that CMF conference for the first time that year! I continued to pray for my prospective partner without knowing who it is, and it took a few more years before God made it clearer for me!

Passing the final examination from medical school was a turning point in my life. There was a year of mandatory internship and all of us were looking forward to another year on the campus without classes and examinations! This was a time for us to relax, enjoy, and plan for the future. We would be living in the house surgeons' quarters next to the medical college hospital.

Little Did I Know That God Had Other Plans

Seven of us (five men and two ladies), to our utter disappointment, got the letter posting us for an internship at Kottayam Medical College. Downhearted and dejected, we boarded the train from Trivandrum to Kottayam to begin the internship. They were still using the old District Hospital, Kottayam as the *medical college hospital*; it sure was a poor substitute! There was a severe shortage of patient beds and no proper living quarters for the interns. Overcrowded wards where patients were sleeping on the floor under the beds! Even pregnant women had to crawl under the beds to sleep/rest. It took a while for us to get used to changing the wound dressings of patients while on the floor. And there was no end in sight for this unfortunate health care situation!

While I was the intern in surgery, Leya had her surgery rotation in my unit. One day she had to scrub in a case. She scrubbed, was gowned and glowed, and was waiting for the gown to be tied in the back. I saw the need and responded appropriately. By the time we were finished with the case, the story among my friends was that I tied the *knot* on Leya. How I wish it was that easy and that soon. I had not even expressed my interest to her yet!

After completing the internship, I was appointed as a tutor in the Department of Anatomy, helping medical students in the dissection hall and taking classes for them. My time in the Department of Anatomy gave me a chance to learn about the human body in detail, and the mandatory teaching assignments took away my intense fear of public speaking.

I had another assignment in the Department of Surgery, and that lasted only for a short time. Once again, I had to move to a new department—the Department of Forensic Medicine. The head of this department was the police surgeon for the region, and we were conducting autopsies on all cases where death occurred in suspicious circumstances as a result of suicide, homicide, drowning, auto accident, gunshot, stabbing, etc. The police surgeon had many out-of-station consultations for expert opinions, exhumations, examination of sites, skeletal remains, etc.

Often, we had to go to the court of law to testify on the certificates we gave and/or give expert opinions. Even though this was not the vocation of my choice, the time I spent in that department blessed me in many ways.

My head of the department was the best ever; he treated me as a friend while we both knew who the boss was. He valued my input in the management of the day-to-day running of the department as well as teaching assignments. We had many official trips together to hill stations in Kerala. Hundreds of autopsies that I did during this period gave me confidence in my anatomy and a better start in surgery!

Too Timid to Ask

On Christmas Day 2021, we celebrated our fiftieth wedding anniversary. When I look back, I can see God's hand in action in bringing us together. Starting with the totally unexpected move from Trivandrum to Kottayam for internship and the few years of my work in various departments in the medical college, His plan was realized in my life. I was somehow attracted to this young lady who was beautiful in appearance and character. And I started praying for guidance and discernment.

By this time, she had already graduated and got appointed at Mandiram Hospital, Manganam. A good friend of mine decided to take a chance to write a letter to Leya asking if she would consider me for her life partner. This he did without my knowledge. I don't know how long it took for him to get a reply. Of course, there was no yes or no answer there. She stated that she had a good opinion of me, but the marriage proposal has to wait until approved from home!

When I saw that letter, I was elated and took it as my green light to proceed. We started to communicate through letters and very infrequent short phone calls. We learned a lot about each other through these letters, reading and rereading them. I still do not know who was more timid between us, too timid for dating or outings. We both wanted to let our parents know and give us their blessings. I decided to approach my uncle and spiritual mentor, who knew Leya's family well.

After listening to my case, his first reaction was to go to God in prayer. He lifted me in prayer and asked God to close all doors in this matter if it is not in His will. And I said, "Amen!"

I learned a great lesson in prayer that day! In a few weeks, my uncle would go to Mandiram Hospital and interview Leya. My oldest sister, when she came to know about the proposal, she, too, made a quick visit to Mandiram Hospital to spend a few minutes with the busy doctor, soon to be her sister-in-law!

Leya finally confided to her elder brother's wife and waited for the opportune time to tell her mom. After several futile attempts, she decided to wait to talk to her when she was going to be with her at CMC Vellore for her thyroid surgery. The surgery went well and Leya and Mom returned home. She once again lost her chance to tell Mom about me.

Once both sets of parents came to know about our desire, they gladly agreed, and our wedding was set for Saturday the twenty-fifth of December 1971 at Keezhillam Mar Thoma Church. A simple wedding in the traditional Mar Thoma rites followed by a tea party at the St. Thomas High School hall nearby.

Life in Mandiram Campus

Soon after the wedding, we moved into the original home of Leya's dad and siblings on the campus of The Poor Home in Manganam. This is the home where Mr. P. C. George took care of the three younger siblings after the untimely passing of their parents. He was only sixteen and the youngest girl; Leyamma was only seven. There were two boys between them. The older one, Mr. P. C. Chacko, was a teacher, and the younger Rev. P. C. Cheriyan, is my father-in-law, a pastor, and a teacher.

Mr. P. C. George and Leyamma dedicated their whole lives to serving the poor and the needy while witnessing God's love to everyone through their manifold sacrificial activities. They used their home to shelter the poor and crippled, and eventually with the help of many friends, started the Poor Home to care for the destitute. Leyamma died contracting cholera while nursing inmates with cholera in the poor home. She was only thirty-one. Mr. P. C. George continued with his service. He was instrumental in starting the Mandiram Hospital and initiating many services and educational activities.

During our stay in that home, I got the opportunity to talk to and learn from many men and women who had a close association with George and Leyamma. I was amazed at the way the Almighty used those orphans in a little-known village to do miraculous things for their fellow human beings. Many years later, my long desire to publish their biography came to fruition when *Orphans of Mundakapadam* was published here in the United States and also in India.

Tanzania, Here We Come

I enjoyed every job that I had thus far, but none of them gave me the satisfaction of choosing it as my vocation. We were praying for guidance from God and an opportunity showed up to apply for a job under the government of Tanzania. We received my appointment order with instructions to make travel arrangements. Our joy was doubled when we realized that our first baby was to show up in less than nine months!

Leya contracted chicken pox and was laid up for a couple of weeks. A week before the date for our travel, I, too, got chicken pox and was miserable for a few days. Finally, in September 1972, we made our flight to Dar es Salaam via Nairobi.

We stayed in a nice hotel there for two weeks awaiting our assignment to a hospital. I was appointed to the Regional Consultant Teaching Hospital, Mwanza, and we took the flight to this beautiful city on the banks of Lake Victoria. The newly constructed hospital building was nine stories high, and it stood on the top of Bugando Hill, overlooking the lake. Tanzania, Kenya, and Uganda, which constituted the East African Union, formed the boundaries for Lake Victoria. Ferry boats transported goods and passengers across the lake. In Mwanza, the lakeshore was busy on weekends and evenings with people walking along and peddlers selling souvenirs and snacks.

Mwanza Hospital was one of the four regional hospitals in the country. The hospital was originally built by the German missionaries but was soon taken over by the government of Tanzania. It was staffed with consultants from many European countries as well as from the USA. A few doctors like me were recruited by the government of Tanzania. There was a school of nursing as well as a school for the medical assistants operational in this teaching hospital. Several housing units were available on Bugando Hill around the hospital, and the rest of the staff had their accommodation provided in nearby housing units. We had our apartment at Ismillo Hills, about four miles from the hospital.

My initial viewing of the hospital from the front yard was breathtaking. This massive skyscraper majestically standing on top of the hill was not the mental picture I had of a hospital in East Africa. We were given a tour of the facility, and it sure was impressive. Met with the medical and paramedical staff from all across the globe. Physicians from at least thirteen countries! USA, UK, Belgium, Netherlands, Germany, Yugoslavia, USSR, Portugal, Ireland, Norway, India, Ethiopia, and Tanzania. It was a small United Nations! Soon we would get to know them all closely and develop lasting friendships with many.

Dr. Kimati was the head of the Department of Pediatrics and was well trained in the UK and was a Fellow of the Royal College of Physicians. When he learned that Leya is interested in pediatrics, he took her under his wing. While we were staying in the Lake View Hotel in downtown Mwanza awaiting allocation of our housing, it was Dr. Kimati who gave us rides to and from the hospital every day. The Department of Pediatrics was very busy with all sorts of tropical diseases like malaria, tetanus, marasmus, kwashiorkor, gastroenteritis, Burkitt's lymphoma, and burns as well as fractures. Leya got busy learning and sharpening her knowledge in pediatrics by following Dr. Kimati at patient rounds, even before she was officially appointed as a medical officer there.

I was interested in surgery, and I got posted to the Department of Surgery. As a junior medical officer, we had to take care of cases in all specialties, including internal medicine as well as obstetrics and gynecology. Dr. Monach was a surgeon from Holland. Dr. Magda Van Hoywheghen, a board-certified surgeon from Belgium and trained in New York, joined us a few months after our arrival in Mwanza. Soon a team of surgeons, internists, ophthalmologists, and anesthesiologists from the USSR joined us. Even though the basics of medicine remain the same all across the globe, the philosophy, ethics, and the social and cultural impact on the physician varied much from continent to continent, and often from one region to another in the same continent. Again, working with this mini United Nations under one roof was an unforgettable experience for my wife and me.

Magda Van Hoywheghen was a true mentor to me in surgery. She had just finished her formal training in surgery in the United States under Dr. John L. Madden, one of the prominent surgeons of that time. Every time I scrubbed in a case with Magda, she would start talking about how Dr. Madden would do that procedure and what sort of questions he would ask his residents during the surgery. Little did I know then that I was being prepared for my days ahead in training in surgery under Dr. Madden!

I successfully took the examination for qualification for applying for training in the USA (ECFMG) at Dar es Salaam, Tanzania. I still had about seven months remaining in my contract to serve the government of Tanzania.

One morning while making rounds in the hospital, Magda turned to me and said, "Mathew, I received a letter from Madden. He will have a position for you in the residency program starting in July 1975."

If I say that I was surprised, it would be an understatement; I had never asked Magda to request Dr. Madden for a place in the program, and I never knew that she had written to him on my behalf!

We were thrilled at the prospect of getting a chance to go to New York and pursue our dream vocational training! We had to make a decision pretty soon. Joining the program in July meant breaking the contract with the government of Tanzania, forfeiting all the monetary benefits that I'm entitled to at the end of contract, and paying back the money that they had spent on our initial trip from India to Tanzania. Once we made the decision to join and let the residency program director know, we were given our appointment order.

We sold our used car and all the pots and pans and anything valuable that we owned to generate funds to buy the tickets as well as to pay back the money to the government of Tanzania. We traveled to Dar es Salaam, had the interview at the US Consulate for the visa, and got our contract canceled at the ministry of health (vizier ya affia).

We left Mwanza on the twentieth of May 1975, a day before our daughter turned two. (That way we did not have to buy a separate ticket for her.) We went back to India and spent a few weeks with our parents and siblings, giving all of them a chance to see our baby for the first time.

On June 26, our Air India flight from Bombay Airport took off around midnight, stopped in New Delhi, and took off from there. After flying an hour, the pilot made the announcement, "Due to technical issues, we are forced to return to the base."

Soon, the Boeing 747 made a 180-degree turn, and we were again back at the Delhi Airport around 2:30 a.m. Only after landing were we told that the plane had major engine trouble and that we need to wait for a replacement plane to take us to New York. The immigration authorities had all our passports, and we were driven to a luxury hotel for accommodation. We had not even a change of clothes for us or the baby. All our baggage were not in our possession! To make matters worse, that was the night Ms. Gandhi declared emergency status in the country. There was a total blackout for television/radio or newspaper news. We waited patiently, often going to the front desk to check for the next flight. Finally, on the twenty-eighth, we boarded another Air India flight and landed in JFK Airport, New York that evening.

Thanks to the generosity and hospitality of a few of our friends, we did not have any trouble settling down in the City That Never Sleeps. I moved into a room on the sixth floor of St. Clare's Hospital in midtown Manhattan on June 30, 1975. Leya and Maya stayed with our good friends George Mathew and Valsa in Long Island for several days before we were allowed to move into an apartment owned by the hospital and next door to it.

Surgical residency was tough, maybe a bit tougher than I expected. It was a four-year pyramidal program. We had sixteen first-year residents, eight for second year, four for third year, and only three for the senior year. All those who were eliminated would look for positions elsewhere in surgery, surgical specialties, and sometimes in any other specialty like internal medicine, pediatrics, psychiatry, etc. By God's grace, I was able to complete my residency in the same program.

Leya stayed home with the baby for a year, successfully completed her ECFMG certification, and was ready to start her residency in pediatrics. Unfortunately, she did not get selected initially. When a vacancy came in the surgical program, Leya was given that position. Soon, a resident in the pediatric program in St. Clare's failed to come back from her vacation, and this cleared the way for Leya to apply for that position and get into her chosen specialty training program.

So we both completed our training on June 30, 1979, and started driving out of Manhattan that evening with all our possessions in a tiny U-Haul trailer hitched to the back of our car!

Manhattan, New York to Gramercy, Louisiana

St. Clare's Hospital and Health Center in midtown Manhattan was a great place for residency training in general surgery. Knife and gun clubs on Forty-Second Street and around provided more than enough variety of trauma for the surgical residents of St. Clare's. As there was no residency in orthopedics and urology services in this facility, all these specialties were managed by surgery residents, who thereby gained a wide range of experience in general surgery. Initially, under Dr. John L. Madden and later on under William F. Mitty Jr. MD, there was good teaching and guidance in training. The surgery residents also had the opportunity to rotate through Mayo Clinic in Rochester, Minnesota in cardiovascular surgery and in Sloan Kettering Hospital in New York for oncological surgery.

I would not have traded this place for anything else for surgical training. I would not consider Manhattan for the practice of surgery or for raising a family.

It was around the middle of March 1979 that I started looking for a job opportunity once I finished my residency training at the end of June. I sent my resume to a placement agency in Boston and within a short time got a call from New Orleans regarding a practice opportunity. An administrator of a hospital in New Orleans was trying to recruit a surgeon and an internist to start a practice in a small community between the two major cities—New Orleans and Baton Rouge. He wanted my wife and me to fly to New Orleans and visit the place. As Leya was pregnant with our second daughter, she decided to stay back and send me to go and have a look at the opportunity. I made that trip, fell in love with the place, and the rest is history.

A Tale of Crawfish Tails

Often people ask me what brought me from Manhattan to this tiny town in South Louisiana, and my answer is *crawfish*. When I landed at the New Orleans Airport, I was received by the administrator and his assistant who drove me toward Lutcher. Driving along the bayous and cane fields, seeing men and women sitting along the banks of the small waterways with fishing rods in their hands and the greenery all along the way was a relaxing experience for me. I was looking for a way out from the city of concrete towers and streets teeming with the unfriendly and impersonal crowd going at a very fast pace.

Midway to our destination, we stopped for lunch. Airline Motors restaurant was a landmark for many years. As we walked into the dining area to be seated, I was struck by the sight of orange-colored mini lobsters heaped on the middle of a table that was surrounded by a few men seated on chairs. One of them obviously heard me asking my friend what this creature was, and he responded by offering me a sample from the heap for tasting. He peeled the shell and gave me the tail meat, and I ate it. That did it and I was ready to sign the contract!

A two-year contract to cover the emergency room at nights and weekends while practicing on weekdays.

A short visit to the hospital and meeting with the medical staff and the administrator gave me a good impression of the people and the place. There was a plan for building a larger hospital in the nearby town, I was told. My contract was for two years at a salary of $5,000/month. They had recruited another physician from New York to share the office and share the emergency room call schedule. Between the two of us, we had to cover the emergency room from 6:00 p.m. to 6:00 a.m. every weekday and from twelve noon on Saturday till

6:00 a.m. on Monday on weekends. During the daytime, we were to see patients in our office and do surgery and make rounds in the hospital.

An old medical office building of a recently retired local physician was leased for us to see patients.

A young girl who had just graduated from high school was hired as our receptionist and a registered nurse to manage the office and assist us in seeing patients. It was a slow start for the new surgeon in the community. Who can blame people staying away from a newcomer into their community who wanted to do surgery on them? I have not forgotten the first patient whom I had worked up for her abdominal pains and diagnosed gallstones. When I recommended gallbladder surgery, she wanted to be sent to Ochsner Hospital in New Orleans. I had to keep my ego down and give her a referral to the larger facility!

Patients who were brought to the emergency room did not always have the luxury of going to larger hospitals. I started getting some patients with stab wounds, broken bones, and even gunshots. Few appendicitis cases and some patients with a hernia gave me a chance to break in. All the family practitioners at the facility used to do some surgery also in addition to delivering babies, and a few of them did C-sections too.

After my arrival, a couple of them decided to stop doing surgery and started sending their patients my way. Pretty soon I was getting busier in the office and the operating room, and the emergency room coverage every other day became a tough chore with no end in the near future. Hiring residents from New Orleans hospitals to moonlight in our hospital was an option they had and that they had promised us. This did not happen soon enough, and even when they started getting some, it was way far in between. The internist who was hired with me decided to break his contract and leave. He found a practice in Fort Worth, Texas, and moved. After completing a year of my contract, I, too, wanted to get out of my contractual obligations on the grounds that I did not have another physician to share my calls anymore. After thirteen months, I was relieved of the contractual obligations. Now I can be my own boss!

I got the contract with the hospital to provide physicians to cover the emergency room. Started getting physicians to come and moonlight. I also took my share of calls. The second year in the new place was a lot busier and better than the first.

IRS Audit?

Did I mention that during the time when we were working under the original contract, all the revenue that was generated from the practice was going to an account that was opened in the local bank? I did not have the check-writing privilege and had no idea as to the account details. The only monetary benefit that I had was my $5,000/month salary check that was signed by the accountant and general partner of the business. I was so relieved when the contract was over, and I got the freedom.

Getting a registered letter from the Internal Revenue Service asking me to produce the details of the account for the initial year of my practice was a shock indeed. I had no idea as to how much my practice had generated and how the funds were disbursed. After putting a lot of thought and sleepless nights, I decided to write a detailed reply to IRS and requested an audience at their office. I got the appointment. With the two-page letter in my hand, I faced the IRS official at her office in New Orleans.

This IRS Officer, an African American lady, read my letter with patience and looked like she believed my story. She wanted the contact number of the administrator and his assistant. She made the call while I was sitting in her office and asked that the administrator should appear in her office with all the documents. Then she turned to me and said, "This is as far as I can do. If he comes with all the documents, you will be free. If not, you will hear from me."

Thank God I did not hear from her anymore!

Midtown Manhattan to Lutcher/Gramercy, Louisiana Culture Shock!

Over ten million people move around in Manhattan at a fast pace, and the city never sleeps. Ambulance and police cars roam around blaring their siren and flashing their lights. Even the next-door neighbor refuses to acknowledge your presence in this city of over ten million total strangers. Often, people view each other with suspicion, and if one person attempts to talk to you, you better keep your hands in your pockets and walk fast. This is the usual etiquette of city life.

The Lutcher-Gramercy complex is formed by two cities in Louisiana with no geographical boundaries. Both cities have their own mayor and city council, own sheriff and police, and people take great pride in their city. Culturally and socially, these are two distinct cities. The total population of the twin cities—under three thousand! There was only one traffic light on Main Street for the whole area. More than ten vehicles on the road were considered traffic jams here.

People in South Louisiana are extremely friendly and very eager to know everything about everyone. In this predominantly Catholic community, most families have been calling it their home for many generations. It was very unusual to see people moving out to other states or even other cities for better job opportunities.

First of many things. First surgeon and first pediatrician to settle in the community, first Asian Indian in the community, and the only brown child in the whole school. Fortunately for our daughter, the Montessori school training in New York helped in her new school. Within a few weeks of joining in the first grade at Chanel

Parochial School, the headmistress, Sister Andrea, called us asking if it is okay for our daughter to be placed in second grade! And she was promoted to second grade.

We as newcomers to this Southern Louisiana setup had to learn a lot of things fast to get used to and get assimilated into the new community. Parental involvement in the school was something that we had no experience with. When our daughter came home with an assignment to do a science project, we didn't know what to say. Little did we know the role parents play in guiding children in these assignments.

Science project for the children—or was it for the parents? As parents of a child in grade school, we had to face many issues that were totally new to us. Science project was one. Each student had to come up with a science project and compete with the rest of the class. We had no idea that it was mainly the parents who were doing the major share of the project and letting the children present it as his/hers at the competition.

All that I could come up with was letting our daughter make the replica of a telephone by attaching two soup cans with a string and presenting it at her second-grade class competition. Needless to say, her project was the source of too many jokes and ridicules. By the following year, both the parents and the daughter learned a bit about science projects.

Groundbreaking for a New Hospital in LaPlace, Louisiana

Plans for a new hospital in the nearby township were in the minds of several physicians in the community for quite some time. Groundbreaking to begin the construction of the new hospital was a memorable event. I had the opportunity and the privilege to work with the founding leaders of the medical staff in formulating the bylaws as well as the rules and regulations for the new hospital. We spent many evenings writing and rewriting these very important documents for our hospital soon to be opened.

River Parishes Medical Center was officially opened in June 1982. This one hundred and twenty-five-bed hospital on LA 61 and not far from Interstate 10 was a dream that came true for the residents and the physicians of this community alike. This multispecialty hospital was ready to provide for the total basic health care of the community. The medical and surgical units were on one side and the OB-GYN and pediatric units on the other side. The emergency room was staffed by well-trained physicians and was open twenty-four hours a day and seven days a week. The operating rooms and obstetrics suits were modern and well equipped, so were the laboratory and radiology departments as well. The physicians' office complex was soon to be built close to the hospital building. Temporary office space was provided in trailers for each physician who was recruited.

Dr. Mohammed Suleman, a general surgeon from Kenner, Louisiana, joined the department. Dr. Wayne Robichaux from LSU was the third surgeon to join the department. A couple of internists, a few family practitioners, two obstetricians, and two pediatricians were there initially. Dr. Bijan Motaghedi, an ENT specialist, and Dr. Tong C. Lee, a gastroenterologist, also were among the initial group. Dr. David S.t Germaine, an internist, Dr. Pedrosa, an endocrinologist, also provided specialty care. Dr. V.J. Zeringue was the orthopedic surgeon, and Kelley Stewart was our pathologist. Dr. Farida Baig joined soon as a nephrologist. Dr. Manjit Wadhwa was recruited to be the chief anesthesiologist. Mr. George Foss was the chief executive officer throughout the construction time and the initial period after it has opened.

A multiethnic group of medical staff was a novelty for this South Louisiana community. There were doctors of Indian, Pakistani, Persian, Columbian, and Taiwanese origin providing various specialty care in their fields to a community that was used to getting their sole health care needs through a few local family practitioners. The community welcomed the new physicians with open arms while acceptance from some of the local physicians was less than optimal. Some of their prejudices and narrow-minded outlook created some rough ride once in a while.

Ambulance Service

Two parishes on the east bank of the Mississippi River were served by the small parish hospital in Lutcher, and the entire area had one ambulance run by a family in Garyville. Interestingly, they also were the owners of a funeral home for generations. Two essential businesses in any community but with very little competition in small communities like ours. The ambulance was equipped with a stretcher, an oxygen cylinder, face masks and Ambu bags and splints, and a few rolls of Ace bandages and clean gauzes. There was no defibrillator, no certified paramedics, but the brother-and-sister team was always ready to assist the needy by providing fairly safe and fast transportation with the flashing lights and screaming siren. This family was an integral part of our small community. They were on call 24-7 and all through the year irrespective of Christmas, New Year, or Hanukkah.

When the new hospital in the nearby community was in the planning stage, in anticipation of expanding business, our friend put some major expansion of his staff and equipment. Another new ambulance was bought, and a couple of new paramedics/ambulance operators were hired. During the first two years, the new hospital made some positive impact on the health-care needs of the community. Specialists in several fields of medicine, which hitherto were unknown to the community, were added. The emergency room attracted a good number of victims of trauma from motor accidents to gunshots and industrial accidents.

Our little community was growing a bit too fast. Mom-and-pop stores which used to care for every need of the community were challenged by the huge chain stores that provided everything one can imagine under one roof. They were able to provide everything you needed at a cheaper price by bringing them in bulk from producers as far away as China. One by one our mom-and-pop stores went under.

Larger cities on either side of us had their ambulance service provided by a big company that was owned by a large corporation. They had an eye on our community for a while and when the new hospital got busier, they found it their time to get in too. By television advertisements and influencing the local governmental authorities, they went into a major membership campaign, enlisting the citizens to subscribe to the ambulance service under them. The local long-standing ambulance operator was no match for the big guy. They, too, had the same fate as our mom-and-pop store owners! The funeral home business that they were running along with the ambulance service provided a buffer for them when the competition got really tough.

I still remember the many trips that I made in the old ambulance to referral hospitals in New Orleans as well as in Baton Rouge. Any time an unstable patient had to be transported, it was our policy to ride in the ambulance with the patient. At times, a patient would need to be incubated and manually bagged during the ride, but often it was just to give moral support to the operators.

On an evening, someone called me at home requesting me to come to the scene of a car accident down the street where we lived. A six-year-old boy was knocked down unconscious by a passing car. He had a broken femur as well. By the time I reached the scene, the ambulance was there. His lower limb was splinted, a soft collar was wrapped around his neck, and he was placed in the ambulance. With the oxygen given through the nasal cannula, we were ready for a fast ride to Baton Rouge General Hospital, the nearest facility with a neurosurgeon. Though he remained in a coma, the boy continued to breathe on his own and remained stable through the trip to the hospital. We stayed there until the neurosurgeon came and evaluated the patient.

It took a couple of days before I realized that the boy in the accident happened to be my daughter's classmate. She came home with the report that everyone in her school was talking about her dad who *saved* her classmate. It sure was a boost to the new surgeon in town. Sid did well and recovered fully without any neurological deficit and returned to school.

Liability Claims from Unexpected Sources More Cases to Follow

Being in a small community has its own benefits; your good deeds will not go unnoticed. Establishing a good name early in the practice will go a long way in avoiding malpractice suits, I was told. In my case, it did not work quite the same way! That's the reason I recited little Sid's story here.

A couple of years went by; I was getting to be comfortably busy in my practice. One afternoon, a fifty-five-year-old gentleman came to me for consultation for some urological complaints. As part of my examination, I did a urine analysis, and it showed the presence of small amounts of blood. Without much delay, I got him an appointment with a consultant urologist who came to the local hospital every Wednesday. After working him up, the urologist scheduled him for transurethral resection of the prostate (TURP). The patient was admitted to the local hospital and on a Wednesday morning, he underwent TURP under spinal anesthesia.

I visited him after surgery in his room and found him recovering from the surgery and anesthesia. Had a few minutes of conversation with him and his wife. (Did I tell you they were the grandparents of Sid!) That evening when the urologist made postoperative rounds, he found the patient complaining of pain in his right leg, and the leg was cold with no palpable pulse. Immediately a vascular consultation was obtained with a surgeon in a hospital in New Orleans, and he was transferred by ambulance. An angiogram showed blockage of his right common femoral artery. He underwent surgery that night and the leg was revascularized. He had an uneventful recovery from his TURP as well.

Unfortunately, he was left with a foot drop on the right. The family had an attorney as a cousin and apparently, at his advice, they decided to file a malpractice suit against me, the urologist, and the local hospital. When the copy of their claim came to me by registered mail, I didn't know what to make out of it. I ran to my room, closed the door, and sat down. It took a while before I could finish reading the two long legal pad pages listing the allegations against me. They were questioning my training, experience, judgment, and skill. They were blaming the hospital for not supervising me in my job and for their failure to credential me properly. There were claims for delay in diagnosis, they were asking to be compensated for all the medical expenses, the pain and suffering that the patient suffered, the physical disability that he is left with, and also for the companionship that the spouse lost and her suffering from his illness and for the future medical and surgical expenses!

All this just because I happened to be the one who sent him to the urologist, and I was there in his room that afternoon after his surgery. As I mentioned earlier, this was my first malpractice claim, that, too, coming from the grandfather of the boy whom I took care of at the time of his accident in front of his house! Every malpractice claim hurts, but when it comes from someone you least expected to turn against you, it hurts more.

I was in total confusion. I did not know what I could have done differently that would have avoided this. I am in a community that loves me, and I love them too.

There is no running away from here. I wanted to share this with someone, and the first name that came to my mind was that of my older family practitioner friend Sam in the nearby town. I called him and arranged for a meeting at his home that evening.

When I reached his home, he had just finished seeing patients in his office and walked back to his home across the street. One look at me, he could read my emotional turmoil. With his right hand on my shoulder, he led me to his backyard with scores of trees growing along the borders of a well-manicured lawn. We sat on a cement bench under the shade of an oak tree, and it was my turn to tell the story. I narrated the story of the first-ever malpractice claim against me. I told him how bad I felt and how I still felt that all my dealings with this patient were proper and that I was being accused of all the allegations in the petition.

After intently listening to me, the first thing he told me was, "K, this is your first ever malpractice case, and it is natural to feel bad the way you feel now. For the cases now on you won't feel this bad."

What a consolation! "For the cases now on." Did he say that?

He went on to elaborate by saying, "The longer you stay in practice, the more chances for you to get sued. For this only that we carry malpractice insurance."

And then he narrated the several claims that were brought against him during his long years of practice. Most of them were of no merit and did not cost his insurance carrier much to defend. He also told me in detail how the Louisiana law requires the case to be reviewed by a medical review panel consisting of three physicians of your specialty before it ever goes to trial. My insurance company will be allotting the case to an attorney who will be contacting me and talking to me soon. Then they will arrange to have a meeting with me, take my deposition, and review all the pertinent medical records in this case both from the hospital and from my office.

The plaintiff's attorney may have a lot of questions for me during my deposition, and I will be prepared for all these by my attorney. I can nominate someone in my specialty from the area to the medical review panel, the plaintiff will nominate another physician, and the attorney chairman of the panel will nominate a third physician. I am not at liberty to discuss anything about this case with the panel members or with anyone else. All these were new to me. He also warned me that the process is going to be slow and could go on for a few years! I learned a lot about malpractice suits in that short time than I ever did so far in my adult life!

Surely that friendly encounter with a senior physician helped me a lot to deal with the encounters to follow.

Sure enough, it was a very slow process. Two officials from the insurance company came to have a meeting with me at my office.

They wanted me to write up a summary of the case for them. They also wanted copies of all my office records for this patient. They gave me specific instructions that I should not make any corrections or alterations in the records. Before leaving the office, they gave me their cards with telephone numbers and addresses asking me to contact them for any questions.

It took a while before the medical review panel was formed. I named a surgeon from the nearby hospital to represent me at the panel. Though the medical review panel did not find us deviating from the standard of care, the plaintiff decided to go on with filing the suit. After a period of silence, there was an offer to settle the case outside the court. My insurance company finally settled the case out of court by paying $50,000 to the plaintiff.

My first malpractice case would follow me for the rest of my years in practice. Every time I apply for hospital privileges, every time any hospital staff membership comes for renewal, every time a new insurance company application is filled up, whether it is new or for renewal, every time I apply for a license to practice or to renew it, this incident will have to be mentioned and referred to.

By the time this case was settled, I was threatened with another claim from a patient. This time, it's a young woman who had an abnormal mammogram. This thirty-eight-year-old woman with a positive family history of breast cancer and a long history of tobacco abuse had a mass effect on her mammogram. The radiologist who read the mammogram recommended needle localization breast biopsy. After examining the patient and reviewing the mammogram, I concurred with the radiologist's recommendation and scheduled her for breast biopsy. On the day of the proposed surgery, she called the hospital and canceled the surgery. Next time I heard from her was when I received her malpractice claim against me and the radiologist, accusing us of conspiring to do unnecessary surgery. Unlike the first case, I was not worried about this claim. Sure enough, it did not go even up to the medical review panel. It just faded away! But for the insurance company, it sure was a case against me—claim number two!

Another year went by. One evening, a sixty-year-old gentleman was brought to the local hospital following a blast injury to his right hip. A metal head from a gas cylinder blew off and hit him on the right hip while he was at work at the nearby plant. He had a fracture dislocation of his right hip. After reviewing his X-rays and stabilizing him, I made an orthopedics consultation over the phone and arranged to transfer him to the larger community hospital that was fifteen miles away. I followed him to the hospital and assisted the orthopedic surgeon in his surgery. The patient was admitted to ICU in stable condition. Two days after admission while he was still in ICU, he was diagnosed with acute appendicitis, and I did an appendectomy on him. He had an uneventful recovery and was discharged from the hospital. I saw him for postoperative follow-up visits too.

Later on, he, too, turned around and sent me a malpractice claim for delay in diagnosis, causing pain and suffering as well as nerve damages. Fortunately, this case also did not cause me to lose any sleep. A few months after I received his claim, his original attorney left the state, and he could not find anyone else to take his case. I did not think much about this case either, until one day I received a letter from my insurance company by registered mail. They wanted to review my cases as I reached their threshold of three claims.

By this letter, they were asking me to appear for a "friendly" interview with the board on a specified afternoon. As this was going to be a "friendly encounter," I was instructed specifically not to have any attorney representation for me at this meeting. When I arrived at the insurance office, I was led into a large boardroom. All the board members have already seated around in a C-shaped formation, and I had my chair right in front of them. Even the seating itself was intimidating. The chairman welcomed me and thanked me for coming and then asked me to explain the three claims against me. As soon as I started with the first case where the patient developed pain in his right lower extremity after his urological procedure, one of the board members, the largest among them, shouted out at me, "And you just sat there watching his leg getting rotten, didn't you?"

I knew this was not the "friendly interview" that I was looking for. I replied, "No, sir, he was transferred to a referral hospital for a vascular surgery consultation."

I felt so humiliated that day by a bunch of "high-ranking" insurance board members. I left the office debating who is worse: the one who sued me or the one whom I pay to protect me when sued!

In a couple of days, I got a letter from my insurance company. The board had decided to levy a 33 percent surcharge to my annual insurance premium (just because I had three claims, regardless of their merits). I had made up my mind too—to find another company who would do a better job than this one did!

It was not too hard to find another insurance company to underwrite a policy for me. The premium was comparable to the one I was paying to the physician-owned company from Louisiana, of course, before the surcharge that they were planning. Unfortunately for me, this new company also folded within two years of my joining.

My friend, the ambulance driver, died in a car accident the day I was celebrating my fiftieth birthday.

My fiftieth birthday party was a total *surprise* to me. On that New Year's Eve, we all got dressed up to go to the home of our close friend and office nurse, Irene, for dinner. When we arrived at the place, I found it strange to see all the cars that were parked around her house. As we pressed the doorbell, someone opened the door, and I could not believe my eyes or ears. All our friends had gathered in that house and their shouts of "Surprise!" was deafening. We had fun with good food, great company, and entertainment. Dr. Joe La Nasa had brought his clarinet and played a few songs on it.

Close to midnight, we called it off and then only I realized that my family had other plans to follow. They were going to drive off to Gatlinburg, Tennessee that night! That is exactly what we did. While driving off, we heard the police and ambulance siren. Little did we know that our good friend and the ambulance driver/owner Earl died in a car accident while we were celebrating my birthday!

The longer one stays in practice, the more chances one has to get sued. I had my share of threats of malpractice suits. Majority of them were frivolous and of no consequences. Still, any time the patient compensation company sends you a registered letter letting you know that there is a threat of litigation, an uneasy feeling goes through your mind. Often it is from the least expected sources that these claims come. In my long career in practicing surgery, I had my share of complications and unforeseen outcomes. None of these patients ever thought of suing me. Like the first litigation that came from the grandfather of the kid whom I helped by going out of my way, it is often from the least expected source that litigation comes.

Surgeons as a whole do not have a long-standing relationship with patients whom they operate for the first time. They are usually sent to his office by another physician or seen in the emergency room for consultation. In the majority of cases, the patient undergoes surgery before he can establish a long-standing relationship with the surgeon. If the results are not perfect or some complications happen, these patients can easily turn around and file a liability suit. In the primary care specialties where the doctor-patient relationship has been established, they will hesitate a bit before filing the suit.

A fifty-year-old woman was referred to my office by an internist friend of mine. This lady who was complaining of upper abdominal pain for a long time was worked up. Her ultrasound studies showed *a contracted gallbladder with echogenic shadows consistent with gallstones.* She had an upper midline scar in the abdomen which she attributed to surgery for her peptic ulcer disease over ten years ago at the charity hospital in Baton Rouge, Louisiana. She volunteered the information that her old medical records are not available due to litigation. She was scheduled for gallbladder surgery.

At surgery, we found a lot of scarring in her upper abdomen. After carefully removing all the scar tissue from the area, we found that the gallbladder had already been removed. The patient had an uneventful recovery. She came up with litigation for unnecessary surgery.

Most often, it is not the major surgery or a major setback or complication that results in litigation. I had a thirty-five-year-old male seen in my office with multiple fatty tissue growths on his back. These were surgically removed, and the patient was discharged. I was in total surprise to receive a notification from the patient compensation department of the litigation from this patient claiming compensation for pain and suffering as well as the scars from surgery.

This obese woman in her late forties was referred to me with a mass in her breast which was suspicious for malignancy. An open breast biopsy was done as an outpatient. She had a thin rubber tubing placed in the wound for draining any blood that may collect in the depth of the wound. When she returned for her office visit four days later, the drain was not sticking out of the wound. On questioning her, she said it fell off while she changed the dressing over the incision. The wound healed and the sutures were removed during her next office visit. As the biopsy report was negative for cancer, no further surgery was indicated.

A mammogram in a year at another facility revealed the drain still in the breast tissue. This necessitated another surgery to get the drain removed by another surgeon. Her litigation against me for leaving the drain in the breast arrived in the mail. Fortunately, the medical review panel ruled in my favor, as I had documented her statement that the drain had fallen out while changing the dressing at home. Moreover, the safety pin that was at the outer end of the drain (to prevent it from retracting into the wound) was not on the piece that was seen in the mammogram. She had cut the drain close to the skin and thereby caused it to retract back into the wound!

A young lady who had laparoscopic gallbladder surgery developed severe upper abdominal pain about a week after her surgery. Her workup revealed evidence of some bile leak from the undersurface of the liver from where the gallbladder was dissected out. She needed another surgery to wash out all the bile from around the liver and clean up the raw area under the liver, which by that time had stopped leaking. There was no injury to the major bile ducts and no cause for any further concern. A bile leak like this can happen in any gallbladder surgery. My next medical liability claim was from this lady. She was looking for compensation for all the pain, suffering, loss of income, and disability.

This woman who wanted to sue me was complaining that I refused to do surgery on her because of her smoking habit. She claimed that I was discriminating against her and therefore I should be disciplined. In fact, this lady with many years of heavy smoking habit had a hernia for a long time. As this was clearly an elective procedure that carries high risk with her compromised lung condition, I advised her to stop smoking for at least a few weeks before scheduling for the surgery. This has been my practice with all patients with a smoking habit. I was able to make many a patient quit smoking for good. Fortunately for me, this claim did not go any further up.

Touring the Holy Land Including Boating in the Sea of Galilee

It was a longtime dream that came true for me when we set out for a ten-day tour of the Holy Land in November 2007. My oldest sister had visited the Holy Land in 1961. I treasured her letters from that tour for a long time. She described the two-thousand-year-old olive trees in the garden of Gethsemane, the Church of Nativity, the garden tomb, the tomb of Lazarus, and the boating in the Sea of Galilee so vividly that I wished I could put my feet over those holy places where Jesus walked with his friends a couple of thousand years ago. We had made plans to go for a tour over seven years ago, but the trip was canceled at the very last minute due to the political unrest and unsafe traveling conditions in the area at that time.

A good friend of ours from New York with his wife had invited us to join them on this tour that was arranged by a travel agent they knew. This couple was the only two that we knew among the party of twenty-six that had signed up for this tour. All of them happened to be from the state that we came from and in a day or two, we all became best friends with each other. We had a wonderful time touring Israel and Jordan before returning to New York on the fourteenth of November.

Being a tour that was organized by a travel agent with no affiliation to any religious organization, we did not have clergy on our tour. Walking through the holy ground which gave birth to the three major monotheistic religions i.e., Judaism, Christianity, and Islam, the very first day, most of our team felt the need for a time for reflection at the end of the day. We met in the suite of our leader after dinner and started to talk about our experience of the day. All of us on our tour were Christians, and we experienced the stories from the Bible coming alive over this holy ground.

Soon there was the singing of hymns followed by a reading of passages from the Bible and prayer. Most of the places of biblical importance were marked by the presence of a church over that spot. Most tour groups with clergy were having a mass or a time for prayer and reflection at these spots. At the garden tomb, the experience of seeing the empty tomb, personally going in and coming out, was a moving experience for me. I took the opportunity to read a portion of the gospel and gave a short message to our group there.

Another memorable experience was boating in the Sea of Galilee. There were music and orchestra on board, and all of us enjoyed the ride. Before the end of the ride, our guide, who had listened to my message at the garden tomb, asked me to give another message. What an honor and privilege to be asked to give a sermon over the Sea of Galilee! And I did. A short sermon based on the gospel story of the resurrected Christ making a special trip to the shore of the Sea of Galilee and restoring Peter to discipleship that he had lost by denying his Master three times on the night of his trial. At the end of the boating, we, too, heard the call from the Master asking us if we loved him more than everything else. Thus, it was a wonderful experience for me on that tour of the Holy Land.

Little did I know that while we were enjoying our tour, my patient was being admitted to the hospital with some complications following the surgery that I performed. I had no way of knowing that this lady was going to sue me for medical malpractice and drag me into the court of justice.

By the year 2009, I had been in private practice for thirty years and had been the target of many liability claims. But one can never get used to it. Getting served with a registered envelope from the patients' compensation fund is always an ominous sign. It happens at the least expected time. I had just finished seeing my last patient for the day at the Gramercy office when the letter was delivered to my table. I could very well guess that it was a medical malpractice claim but could not guess who did it. After closing the doors, I reluctantly opened the envelope and glanced at the top of page number 1, which read, "Beatrice Black vs. Karippelil E. Mathew and St. Elizabeth Hospital…"

Following that, there was a litany of allegations against me, starting with doing unnecessary surgery, causing injury to bile ducts, causing liver failure and pancreatitis, and further major surgeries causing disfiguring scars and prolonged disability and loss of companionship, etc. And St. Elizabeth Hospital was also liable for not supervising their surgeon and preventing this outcome.

The story of this particular patient immediately flashed back in my memory. This was a surgery that I had performed almost two years earlier, and they filed the petition just before the two-year limit for making the claim and thereby beating the clock.

I remembered the story of Beatrice Black and her husband Don. They were evacuees from New Orleans after the Hurricane Katrina disaster. They got relocated to Gramercy and were living in a temporary shelter. Ms. Black was seen by one of the primary care physicians in the community for the complaints of her long-standing abdominal pain and nausea. She had a thorough workup including a CT scan of the abdomen, ultrasound study of the gallbladder, and all the necessary laboratory tests. A diagnosis of gallstones and cholecystitis was made, and she was asked to see a surgeon for getting the gallbladder surgery done. She then consulted another primary care doctor who also recommended a surgical consultation and gallbladder surgery. A third physician from the second doctor's office sent her to see me.

I checked her, checked all the reports, and recommended gallbladder surgery. She was scheduled for gallbladder surgery at St. Elizabeth Hospital. She signed the consent forms, and she was sent home with all the necessary papers. Ten days later, I performed a laparoscopic gallbladder surgery on Ms. Black. She happened to have a lot of scar tissue in her abdomen from her previous surgeries as well as several episodes of gallbladder *attacks*. This made the surgery technically difficult, and at one point, there was abrupt bleeding from the area of the artery going into her gallbladder. This was brought under control using clips. She went home the same day of surgery but returned to the emergency room the next day complaining of chest pain and shortness of breath. She was admitted to the hospital and was kept there for a day and discharged home. I saw her at the Gramercy office five days later, and her sutures were trimmed and sent home with advice to see me in two weeks.

It was time for me to go for a Holy Land tour which we had scheduled a long time back. While we were enjoying the tour of the Holy Land, Ms. Black got sick and was readmitted to St. Elizabeth Hospital. After I returned from vacation, I learned that Ms. Black had developed jaundice, and she had to be transferred to Ochsner Foundation Hospital for gastroenterology consultation after a failed ERCP attempt at St. Elizabeth Hospital. I called Don Black and learned that Ochsner Hospital's first attempt at ERCP was unsuccessful, and they were going to do it again the next day. I thought we had a nice conversation, and I promised to keep in touch with him to see how she does the next day or two.

My phone calls were not answered from that day on.

Hatred Hurts You and You Only!

Monday, the thirtieth of July 2012, was the long-awaited day at the court for me to face the plaintiffs and their attorneys bringing all sorts of allegations against me. My conscience was very clear, and I knew that I did not do anything wrong to hurt Ms. Black. And I had no doubt that the allegations were all false. As the day got closer, I tried hard not to hate the plaintiff and her attorneys. That Sunday morning while attending the church service, this feeling came up very strongly in my mind.

At the end of the service, the pastor made the usual altar call. That morning, there was a strong urge from my heart to go forward to the altar and ask for prayer, and I did just that. After spending a few moments alone, I asked the pastor to pray with me that I would not have any hatred in me toward my accusers during the upcoming trial. Putting his hands over my shoulders, that is exactly what my pastor prayed. It felt like a huge burden lifted up from my heart at the end of his prayer, and I was ready to face the new day and whatever that would bring on my path!

Even when the plaintiff's attorney was doing her theatrical performance, very eloquently displaying my alleged malpractice in the case, I was able to listen to her without feeling hatred toward her or her client. I always felt bad for Ms. Black, who unfortunately had some unexpected complications following elective surgery. Her surgery was indicated, and the complications she had were one of the known risks of gallbladder surgery, whether it was performed using laparoscopy as in Black's case or the older method of open gallbladder surgery.

It is true that she had additional surgery and a longer recovery period. But for all practical purposes, Ms. Black had recovered from her surgery. It is true that she is presently unemployed, but this surgery should not keep her from resuming her job. The Blacks or their family members, unlike most of my patients from this small community, did not have any previous encounters with my office. It makes a huge difference if there is an established physician-patient relationship as far as malpractice suits are concerned.

In Mrs. Black's case, I had just one encounter with her and her husband in my office prior to her surgery. Even when she got admitted to the hospital with a complication from my surgery, I was out of the station. True, the surgeon who was covering for me did everything I would have done. I was not surprised that she listened to someone who recommended to sue me to get some money! Moreover, a large number of the public believe that they are suing the insurance company. They have no idea as to the many ways in which a suit adversely affects the physician.

All through the trial, I was able to keep my *cool* and answer all questions at examination and cross-examination. After the case was given to the jury and the jury was sent to the room with instructions from the judge, it was long, indefinite waiting for us, both the plaintiff and the defendant along with their family and attorneys.

During this time, there was an interesting incident that is worth mentioning here. When I was returning to the court after a restroom break, I found my wife hugging the plaintiff's attorney. Apparently, the attorney asked her if she was mad at her. That is all it took for my wife to hug her and prove that there was no animosity in her toward the plaintiff or her attorney. This paved the way for me to join them and to have a conversation with Ms. Black, her husband, and their attorneys. Thank God for taking away any feeling of hatred from my heart that day!

A few light moments in the courtroom. Hon. Judge Garry Hastings is a man always in control in his courtroom. He doesn't miss a thing that goes on in the court. At the same time, he has a great sense of humor too.

Even from the very start, this was evident. During jury selection, he was serious in letting the prospective jurors understand the seriousness of the duty that they are undertaking and that they are the ones deciding the case based on the evidence that is presented during the trial. They were asked to leave sympathy to the plaintiff or to the defendant at the door when they go to the jury room to make the decision. Anyone who is prejudiced or has any relationship with any party in the case had to disclose that and get himself excused, as well as any convicted felon or anyone who has any association with the attorneys in the case or the firms they represent. He specifically asked if anyone among them or anyone in their family has been treated by Dr. or Dr. Mrs. Mathew, they should disclose.

At this point, one gentleman stood up and claimed that Dr. Mathew had operated on him, and this made him disqualified for serving as an impartial juror. This was followed by another who had his wife operated on by Dr. Mathew and a third one whose family member was operated on by Dr. Mathew. At this point, a woman stood up and declared that she knew Dr. Leya from the gym and added, "She is a very sweet lady."

The judge asked her, "Will this influence you in your decision-making in this case?"

She responded, "Probably it will" and she, too, got excused.

Another young woman identified herself as a nurse from St. Elizabeth Hospital and got herself excused. I sat there wondering who is going to be left behind to decide my fate in this case.

One man in his late twenties stood up and confessed that he is a convicted felon and got his excuse.

Now the judge wanted to know if there was any animosity or close friendship between any of the prospective jurors. One young man said that he recognizes the older gentleman on the other end of his row as the father of his friend but did not think that would influence his independent ability to make a decision in the case. Another gentleman pointed to the woman at the far end of his row as his ex-wife and on questioning by the judge, he declared that they are best of friends and would not influence each other in decision-making.

The judge declared, "After spending these long days in a room, if this case brings you back together again, I'm not going to be responsible," and we laughed.

Each prospective juror had to declare under oath their name, age, address, marital status, spouse's name, and job status. He really took to task the first gentleman, an accountant, father of four children, who stated that his wife doesn't work. The judge made it very clear to him that she works harder and for longer hours than he does, and no one who followed the accountant dared to say that his wife doesn't work! The youngest among the jury pool was James, twenty-three, going to graduate from LSU the weekend of the trial. He still lives with his parents and was looking forward to his Bahamas cruise after graduation. James had no job in sight and still appeared to be a pleasant happy-go-lucky guy.

After a lot of our prospective jurors were excused, they had to call in more from the pool of prospective jurors, and they had to go through the same type of interrogation. Now the attorneys had their turn to raise objections against any prospective juror. The plaintiff's attorney had a chance to strike three from the pool and so did the attorney for the defense. In the first round itself, the plaintiff's attorney used her three strikes and eliminated three White jurors whom she thought would be more conservative in their views. The defendant's attorney used only one strike.

Now they had to call in jurors from the pool of the judge in the next court, as our list was already exhausted. From the second round, a few more were selected, and finally, ten jurors and two alternate jurors were selected and were seated by 1:00 p.m. on Monday, the first day of the trial. The judge gave detailed instructions to the jurors and stressed the need for secrecy and the need to stay away from the Internet, Facebook, tweeting, and emailing. Court then recessed for lunch break.

When we're assembled in the afternoon, it was the plaintiff's attorney's turn for her opening statement. The performance was truly theatrical. Sitting in the courtroom watching her narrate what horrible things that Dr. Mathew did to her client while performing a gallbladder surgery was not easy. She had an easel set up in the room to display all sorts of charts and photos for the jurors. She started thanking the jurors for taking the time to be here in the court and praising them for their dedication in performing their civic duty.

Then she elaborated the story of her clients, my patient and her husband. Both in the latter half of the seventh decade, both still unemployed since the day of surgery. They were the victims of Hurricane Katrina, their home in New Orleans was flooded, and they were evacuated to St. James parish. She had a janitorial job at the courthouse, and he was employed as a delivery truck driver in New Orleans.

She went to a physician in Gramercy with complaints of some abdominal pain and constipation. After doing an ultrasound and CT scan of the abdomen, he found that Ms. B had a gallstone. She was asked to see a surgeon. But she decided to get another opinion from another family physician in the community. He, too, asked her to see a surgeon and sent her to Dr. Mathew. Dr. Mathew saw her in his office, did not explain to her anything about gallbladder surgery, but scheduled her for laparoscopic gallbladder surgery at St. Elizabeth Hospital, Gonzales. Her client was under the impression that Dr. Mathew was going to take her gallstone out with a laser and never knew that he was going to remove her gallbladder.

At surgery, Dr. Mathew encountered some unexpected bleeding. Instead of trying to find where the bleeding was coming from, Dr. Mathew started to panic and fired staples left and right—*boom, boom, boom, boom.*

This caused damage to her bile ducts and pancreas and liver. He did not do ERCP or cholangiogram and sent her home in a lot of pain. When she returned to the hospital the next day, she was discharged without doing the necessary tests. After this, Dr. Mathew took a vacation and left the area. When Ms. B got sick and got readmitted to St. Elizabeth Hospital, they could not do the ERCP there, and she was sent to Ochsner Hospital. She had several procedures and surgery there which made Ms. B suffer a lot and become disabled. She lost her job and has not been able to get back to work. Her husband also lost his job while taking care of her. He lost his companionship and suffered a lot.

Now it was time for her to go into *show-and-tell.* She pulled out a series of poster-size photos of the plaintiff showing the close-up shots of her operation scars on the belly, the various drainage tubes, and large dressings on her following the surgery. With each picture, she had a caption and narration. For anyone who has a medical background, all these pictures are normal. But did this move bring in some sympathy from the jurors who had no medical background?

It was time for calling in Mr. Black as the first witness. He was sworn in and seated. The plaintiff's attorney started her interrogation. He described the plaintiff's side of the story as clearly as he could, making sure that he made it clear to the jury that Dr. Mathew never cared to tell them that he was going to remove her gallbladder. He never bothered to tell them anything about laparoscopy or any possible risks or complications, and he never obtained consent for surgery from his wife. In contrast to Dr. Mathew, the consultant surgeon at Ochsner Hospital was extremely caring, friendly, and he took the time to sit with them and explain how sick she was and what exactly he was going to do in surgery. As his wife continued to suffer even after her second surgery at Ochsner Hospital, Mr. Black had to stay home with her and help her out. He lost his job, lost his companionship, and suffered a lot of mental anguish because of Dr. Mathew's surgery.

The attorney for the defendant started with his cross-examination. With a few simple questions, he was able to show the jurors how prejudiced Mr. Black was and how confused he was even on simple things.

“Hired Gun” The Expert Witness from the Citadel of Surgery!

As I mentioned in the previous chapter, I did not feel any hatred toward the plaintiff or their attorney during the trial. This, I believe, was the result of my resolution not to feel hatred and my pastor praying with me on the day before the trial. Unfortunately, it was a different story with the “expert witness” that they brought from far off. This young surgeon was hired by the plaintiff from Durham, North Carolina. He was a board-certified surgeon, a hepatopancreatic surgeon from the University of North Carolina. In this country, you can get an expert in any field to support your client for the right price. Watching him testify in my trial was an ordeal as well as a learning experience. He was called in and he took the oath stating that he would tell the truth, the whole truth, and nothing but the truth. After describing his educational qualifications and surgical experience, he was taken in as an expert witness.

From start to finish, one could see that this young man was trying to be loyal to the plaintiff’s lawyers and was ready to pay back for the money. He went to the extent of stating under oath that he would not have operated on Ms. Black as her symptoms were not from gallstones. (Anyone who had a casual review of her chart could see that the pathology report showed chronic inflammation of the gallbladder, and Ms. Black had a stone in her common bile duct also.) He had no hesitation to state that the surgeon had deviated from the normal standards of gallbladder surgery as he had not described in the operation notes defining the *collet triangle* before applying the clip on the cystic duct.

The attorney for the defendant in his cross-examination made him admit that bleeding and injury to bile ducts are known complications of gallbladder surgery and by themselves do not constitute malpractice. He also read the statement from the expert witness from Ochsner stating that "this can happen to the best surgeon on his best day" and he reluctantly concurred.

Plaintiff had their expert witness next. It was the surgeon from Ochsner Hospital, who had operated on Ms. Black and followed her up for three months. His testimony was very precise and to the point. He explained to the jurors the condition of the patient and the surgical procedure that he performed in detail and in a layman's language. He made it very clear that the complication that had happened was nothing out of the ordinary in laparoscopic gallbladder surgery, especially when the surgeon encounters unexpected bleeding like that Dr. Mathew encountered in Ms. Black's case. Even though the total number of clips used in this case was more than usual, he could not call it negligence or medical malpractice.

During the cross-examination by the defendant's lawyer, he agreed to the statement that he had made in the sworn deposition that "this can happen to the best surgeon on the best day," referring to the surgical complication that Ms. Black had.

Even though they had planned to put Ms. Black on the witness stand the first day, she was feeling too tired by the afternoon and the court was adjourned for the day by 6:00 p.m.

Ms. Black was on the witness stand first the next day. After swearing her in, the plaintiff's attorney tried to make her comfortable on the stand and slowly began her interrogation through simple, leading questions. Ms. Black seemed to be comfortable on the stand and answered questions to the attorney's satisfaction. She wanted the jury to hear the story of the surgeon taking Ms. Black through laparoscopic gallbladder surgery without giving the patient any idea that he was going to remove her gallbladder and not just the stones as she thought he would do. Ms. Black had no recollection of signing the consent for surgery either. Through several questions, the attorney brought out the prolonged and painful experiences she had following the surgery and her continued disability till now.

On cross-examination, the attorney for the defendant made it clear through Ms. Black's answers that at least three medical doctors had told her that she had gallstones and that she needed surgery, and they had recommended consulting Dr. Mathew. She admitted to the fact that she had been discharged from the care of doctors at Ochsner Hospital as she had a full recovery from the surgery there.

The defense had one witness and that was a surgeon from Baton Rouge who was on the medical review panel in this case. He had reviewed the medical chart and studied the case in detail. On the witness stand, he stated that the complications that Ms. Black had were nothing out of the ordinary in this kind of surgery and that he did not see failure to meet the standard of care on the part of the surgeon in this case.

On cross-examination, the plaintiff's attorney asked the doctor if he went to lunch with the defendant just before appearing on the witness stand. He had to admit that he sat at the same table with the attorney for the defendant and the defendant, and he himself paid for his meal.

The attorney for the plaintiffs summarizes her case for the jurors as, "The experienced eighteen-wheel driver in a wreck at a red light."

The plaintiff's attorney was in her top form for the presentation of her case to the jurors. She carefully set her posture before the jurors for her theatrical performance one more time. I never thought she was going to sing my praises as a prelude to her summary of the case. She proceeded, "Dr. Mathew, the defendant in this case may be a very experienced surgeon who has been in practice for many years. He may be the nicest person.

"But I want you to listen to this story. This story is about an experienced truck driver. He is licensed to drive the truck, he had driven this road many, many times, he was not under the effect of drugs or alcohol. This particular day he was driving this curvy road. It was raining heavily. The visibility was low and the truck came close to a traffic light and the light turned red for him. Instead of stepping on the brake and bringing the truck to a stop, our driver stepped on the accelerator and passed the red light.

"There was another small vehicle approaching that intersection at the same time. The driver of this old car was on her way home. Obeying all traffic rules and seeing the light green for her, she proceeded to cross the intersection slowly and carefully. The truck came and slammed on her small car and demolished the car and seriously injured the driver.

"Ladies and gentlemen of the jury, the truck driver in this story is the defendant in this case, Dr. Mathew, and the driver of the small vehicle that was demolished is the plaintiff, Ms. Black.

"You heard her story, how much she got hurt in the hands of Dr. Mathew. According to the law, the driver who caused the accident must compensate for the damages that he caused."

The attorney for the defendant was not very animated nor theatrical. His appeal to the jury was to see that the complications Ms. Black had were nothing out of the ordinary, and Dr. Mathew, the defendant, did not deviate from the standard of care. Quoting the statement from the plaintiff's expert witness, he stressed that "this kind of complications can happen to the best surgeon on his best day."

The judge gave detailed instructions for the jurors and sent them to the conference room for jury deliberations.

Waiting for the verdict is not easy. Seems like the time has come to a standstill. Thank God I had my dear wife on my side all through the ordeal. A good friend and nurse from the practice was also in the court by our side as an observer. For the attorneys, this is nothing out of the ordinary. I have heard that the longer the jurors take to come to a verdict, the better for the plaintiffs.

We waited and waited. A full hour and then another thirty minutes passed. Finally, we were called into court. The jury had reached a verdict. The judge asked the chairperson to read the verdict, as we, the defendants and the plaintiffs with our attorneys, waited. There was pin-drop silence in the court when the verdict was read. After a long deliberation, the jury had cleared me of all allegations. The judge will issue the formal judgment in a few days' time, and the court was dismissed.

Looking back, I can see divine guidance all through. I can't ask for a better attorney than the one who was assigned to me by the insurance company. Lean and tall, very mature and calm, the gentleman with a likable personality. On the very first day, he told me not to worry until he tells me otherwise, and that otherwise never happened. Educating the client to prepare for the deposition as well as for the court dates was very important to him. He wanted me to be teaching the jury while answering the plaintiff's attorney's questions.

I experienced divine guidance through the prayers of a few people including my wife and our pastor. Getting the presence of mind to face the plaintiff's attorney's ruthless attack without showing anger, frustration, or sorrow and getting the right words to use in answering her questions can happen with God's help. This is His promise to all His children.

A verdict in the case in my favor did not end the story. The plaintiff's attorney has decided on filing an appeal. A motion to dismiss the decision in the case did not work. Appeal for a retrial also was dismissed. Finally, the burden was off my shoulders.

Looking back, the trials are all learning experiences in life. It teaches you humility and lets you be aware of your vulnerability. It often gives you a new perspective on life. For me, this trial made the decision for retirement easier. I have seen malpractice cases driving doctors to change their specialties, move away from high-litigation states. Some have taken early retirement from the practices they loved. Public humiliation and financial loss add to this when the jury awards six-figure compensation for the unfortunate incident.

Another surgeon friend of mine was the victim a few years ago when the relative of a local official met with some complications from his surgery. My friend was sued and his trial at the local courthouse was agonizing and prolonged for me to watch. (I was asked to be in the courtroom for moral support.) The jury verdict was in favor of the plaintiff, and my friend was devastated from humiliation in public and emotional anguish and financial loss from an interruption in his practice. I was disappointed but not surprised when he and his family packed up and moved away to a faraway state at the first opportunity they got.

Doctors live by the Hippocratic oath that they took in medical school. Their primary aim is for the well-being of their patients. Unfortunately, things can go wrong at any stage of the game. Deviating from the standard of care or negligence in caring for the patients needs to be addressed and the victims compensated. Unreasonable and extremely high jury awards and solicitation by trial lawyers via billboards and news media made a medical liability crisis in the USA. It was not too far in the past that many obstetricians gave up taking care of pregnant women and delivering them and limiting their practice just to gynecology. They need to be watching out for any of the babies they delivered to turn around and sue them even when they have reached adulthood!

The pharmaceutical industry also faces a similar crisis. Millions of dollars and years of research go in before a new drug is released to the public. These drugs are tested and tried elsewhere on a large number of patients before the FDA approves them for release in this country. All the known possible adverse reactions and side effects are described in the package insert. There is *no* drug without any adverse reaction or side effect. Our tendency to sue the pharmaceutical companies for any and all drug reactions can potentially drive the cost sky high and/or drive them out of business.

If only those of us who complain that the cost of medical care is high in the USA do something to ease the liability crisis. I have lost my hope in the legislature to be of much help in this; they themselves are mostly lawyers.

"Whenever they hand you over, don't worry about how to speak or what you will say, because what you can say will be given to you at that moment. You aren't doing the talking, but the Spirit of my Father is doing the talking through you" (Matthew 10:19–20 CEB).

A Blog from the Other Side of the Globe

I was standing in line at the local drugstore counter when a young man came up to me and asked, "Doc, do you remember me?"

Ability to remember names is not one of my strong points. Fortunately, I remembered Mike from several years back. He came to see me in my office with a large mass in his left armpit. Examination revealed a hard mass, the size of a hen's egg, not attached to the chest wall or skin. The only other positive physical examination finding was the presence of a surgical scar below his left shoulder blade. This was from the excision of a black mole a few years ago. His blood count and chest X-ray were all normal.

I scheduled him for an excision biopsy of the mass from the left axilla, and it was done. The biopsy report came back as metastatic melanoma. Search for the primary lesion did not yield any. The surgical scar from his back was excised along with the surrounding subcutaneous tissues, and it did not show any evidence of melanoma.

Divulging the diagnosis of cancer to your patient is never an easy job. When it is aggressive cancer like melanoma that, too, already spread to a large lymph node making the prognosis a lot worse, the surgeon's job becomes harder in dealing with the patient. Mike came to my office upset about his diagnosis and the prospect of going to MD Anderson Hospital in Houston for further treatment. I had just finished reading the blog from my niece's husband in Christian Medical College, Vellore, India.

I clearly remember the day Anne, my niece, got married. Her dad and I were cousins but closer than brothers. She got to know this young man at the medical college, and they got married with blessings from both families. Soon they would start their postgraduate studies in the same medical college, Tarun in surgery and Ann in obstetrics and gynecology. Their days were busy and tiresome, but their enthusiasm was endless.

Tarun developed a somewhat annoying dry cough and decided to get a chest X-ray which showed a mediastinal mass. Workup and biopsy of the mass led to the diagnosis of lymphoma. There is no good time to get the diagnosis of cancer. But when you have just begun with your married life, full of dreams, when you are starting with your postgraduate training that is tough, competitive, and strenuous. "Why now? Why me?"

All had natural reactions and expected questions. Tarun's unwavering faith and the fervent prayers of Ann and their friends and families went a long way in strengthening Tarun's resolve to persevere. And persevere he did. He continued with his chemo treatment and clinic appointments without missing many classes or assignments in his regular postgraduate studies. He started writing blogs describing his tough experience of the day, the way he is coping with it, and the life lesson that he learned. Reading his blog was a means to follow his progress and see his witnessing for the Lord, through his times of trials and troubles.

The day I was talking with Mike, I decided to share the link to Tarun's blog with him. All those memories flashed back in my mind when I faced my patient Mike in the drugstore that day.

Mike had completed his treatment at MD Anderson, and he was doing very well physically. And he added, "I am pursuing a path to Bible school. Thanks for the link to Tarun's blog."

Dear God, help me to see the opportunities that you send on my way. Amen!

Recurrent Upper GI Bleeding from Gallbladder Polyps

This was one of the unusual cases of my surgical career. This sixteen-year-old White male was brought to the emergency room with complaints of abdominal pain and a few bouts of vomiting blood.

His past medical history showed one bout of vomiting blood at the age of twelve and the routine workup at that time was negative. With the provisional diagnosis of a bleeding duodenal ulcer, he was then treated and discharged.

This well-built young man of athletic build had normal vital signs and was clinically jaundiced. His lungs were clear, and the abdomen was soft with no mass palpable. Ultrasound studies of his abdomen showed a contracted gallbladder with some debris and markedly dilated bile ducts. His liver enzymes showed elevated alkaline phosphates as well as high bilirubin.

Diagnosis of obstructive jaundice probably from gallstones, he was taken to surgery for cholecystectomy and possible exploration of the common bile duct. At surgery, the gallbladder was found to be full of soft polyps and the entire biliary tree was dilated and filled with blood clots. On opening the common bile duct, blood clots filling the biliary tree extruded forming the cast of the biliary tree. The gallbladder was removed, the bile ducts were irrigated, and the abdomen was closed with a T-tube draining the common bile duct.

He had an uneventful postoperative recovery and was discharged in three days. The pathology report on the gallbladder was polyposis of the gallbladder. No malignant or premalignant changes were reported.

This case was presented as "Polyposis of the Gallbladder: An Unusual Presentation with Recurrent Upper GI Bleeding" at the Louisiana chapter of the College of Surgeons meeting in New Orleans.

The Wounded Rhino in Serengeti Park

As we get older, we get wiser and often wonder as to what we were thinking when we made some not very wise decisions in our younger days. I have a series in this category. Deciding to ride in a small Toyota Corolla car for an African wildlife safari through the world-famous Serengeti Park in Tanzania tops the list. Our firstborn daughter was a year old when we decided to get her baptized. At that time, we were living in Mwanza, Tanzania. I had a cousin and several good friends in Dar es Salaam where an Indian pastor has agreed to do the baptism at the local Anglican Church.

We rode the train from Mwanza to Dar es Salaam along with a good friend of ours, a contractor by trade, Mr. Cherian and his wife. Our plan was to return to Mwanza via Serengeti wildlife park in a Toyota Corolla that Mr. Cherian bought in Dar es Salaam. As Mr. Cherian drove with three adults and an infant as his passengers, the initial several hours of the trip were enjoyable.

Soon the roads turned rough, and the drive was not smooth anymore. No wonder all the vehicles we saw in the park that day were large four-wheel drives, and we were the only exception. Uneven roads with deep ditches and large rocks like boulders were not intended for a car like the one we were in. We had a puncture in one tire that could be repaired and then a blowout in another.

We were still making slow progress. The park was beautiful, and we enjoyed watching the animals and birds in abundance. It was late in the day, and the sun was going down on the horizon when we took a turn on that curvy road. We came too close to a wild rhinoceros facing us in front of the car. He was wounded and wild.

The car came to an abrupt stop.
Our hearts were pounding fast.
Both the driver and I were sweating.
I could feel the mounting tension in our small Corolla.
Our tiny vehicle was no match for this enormous wild animal!
In a few minutes (though it felt like an eternity at that time), the animal turned around and walked away, letting us go on our way!

A Poisoned Arrowhead Travels from Mwanza to Manhattan

Our thirty-month-long time in Mwanza, Tanzania has etched some memories about the people, their culture, customs, and beliefs. Though their official language is Kiswahili, each tribe speaks its own language. Major religions in Tanzania are Christianity and Islam, and a good number are pagans. They have clinics and hospitals all across the country run by mostly Tanzanian doctors or medical assistants. Four regional consultants and teaching hospitals were providing specialty medical and surgical care. These were in Dar es Salaam, Tanga, Moshi, and Mwanza.

Many Tanzanians were still going to their tribal doctors for all their ailments before going to see a physician practicing modern medicine. Their modalities of treatment varied widely from the use of herbal medications to making surgical incisions on the body to let bad blood out or use of voodoo medicine. Widows in the neighborhood were believed to be witches and were responsible for someone getting sick, dying, or having a miscarriage! It was not unusual for the community to get together and attack the "witch" with a machete, *panga*, or shooting with a poisoned arrow!

An elderly lady was brought to the emergency room one afternoon after she was shot with a poisoned arrowhead. It took two days for men to carry her all the way to the hospital on foot. This emaciated and dehydrated woman was still breathing and had low blood pressure and rapid heart rate. Her chest X-ray showed the arrowhead traversing the left chest cavity across the cardiac shadow. There was a small left-sided pneumothorax (free air outside the lung).

Being on call that night, the responsibility for taking care of this patient rested on my shoulders. I took her to the operation theater and did a left thoracotomy and removed the arrowhead that was stuck on the body of a thoracic vertebra. The chest was closed with a chest tube in place, connected to an underwater seal drainage bottle. The arrowhead was approximately seven inches long, and the herbal stuff that was seen wrapped around its tip was the poison. I kept the arrowhead in my locker as a souvenir.

Dr. Victor C. Delucia, a thoracic surgeon from the USA, came to Mwanza, and he was there to interview Dr. Magda Van Hoyweghen for her fellowship in the American College of Surgeons. Magda delegated me to take Dr. Delucia for a tour of the hospital. While passing through the surgical ward, I presented this lady recovering from the thoracotomy and removal of the poisoned arrowhead from the chest. He was impressed by the case as this was the first time that he was seeing a victim of this kind of trauma. He was more impressed when I presented him with the weapon that I had kept in the locker. Quite an unusual weapon in his hospital in New York!

At this point, it is worth mentioning that Dr. Delucia was the vice-chairman of the surgery training program at St. Clare's Hospital in New York. And this served as my personal interview for residency there later that year! God works in mysterious ways!

Mission Trip Experiences

We are honored, privileged, and excited to share our mission experience with you. We are like Apostle Paul, who when writing to the church in Corinth wrote, "When I came to you…I was with you in weakness, and in fear, and in much trembling."

We pray our testimony will glorify God and will nudge someone to feel the Holy Spirit nudging him/her in the right direction.

When we both decided to go into retirement from our thirty-two years of medical practice here in South Louisiana, it was a time for reflection. A time to reflect on the wonderful ways in which God sent his angels to direct, guide, and protect us in our life's journey. We started counting men and women who helped us to become what we are today. They were there in India where we grew up, they were in Tanzania, East Africa, they were in New York City, and sure many of them were in Louisiana. While growing up, we had Christian parents and older siblings, Sunday schoolteachers and wonderful schoolteachers, missionaries and preachers, and good Christian friends.

In 1972, when we moved to Mwanza, Tanzania, we were amazed by the number of men and women whom God had already arranged there to help us. Among them was Dr. Kimati, a Tanzanian doctor and professor of pediatrics who took Leya, my wife, under his wings to train her in pediatrics. He was there to give us a ride to and from the hospital every morning and evening until we were able to get our own car. There was Dr. Evans, an ob-gyn specialist from the UK who took care of Leya in her first pregnancy and delivery. There was Dr. Myrtle Keller, a gynecologist and a nun from Pennsylvania to care for Leya at a time we needed medical care. And there was Dr. Magda Van Hoyweghen, a nun and surgeon from Belgium to train me in surgery and later on be instrumental in obtaining a position for residency in surgery in midtown Manhattan.

There was Dr. Monach from the Netherlands who introduced us to the Anglican Church in Mwanza, and there were two Baptist missionaries, Jack and Don, who led us in Bible study on a regular basis. There were several other men and women God ordained to help us in various ways while in Mwanza.

His helping hands continued to follow us to New York City where He had arranged Ms. Delia, an elderly Irish lady, to take care of our daughter while we both were busy in residency training. So many in the South Louisiana community helped us.

The list of His angels that He sent on our way is pretty long, and there is no way that we can ever pay back to even part of the favors that they did to us. Some of these men and women have passed away, and some are continents apart. The only practical thing that we could and should decide to do was to *pay forward*—in other words, do the favor to someone else that God brings to our path. Going for short medical missions gave us a chance to give back some to God's children in need.

In addition to the patients we see at clinics or hospitals, often we encounter people in need during these trips.

There was a young lady helping us in our apartment when we did a short mission at Oddanchatram in India. This lady was a single mom whose daughter attended the clinic with acute leukemia. Even in that mission hospital, the cost of chemo treatment is prohibitively high for that poor lady.

At Tenwek Hospital during our last visit, we were assisted at our guesthouse by a Rwandan refugee. Her story was heart-wrenching. She witnessed the killing of her parents and siblings and ran away from her country. She and her husband settled in Kenya and were raising their three daughters when her husband was diagnosed with cancer of the esophagus, and he died. This young lady is struggling to keep her children in school. We met her beautiful children. Intelligent and hardworking, one wants to be a lawyer and another a doctor. Our God who takes care of the birds of the air and the lilies of the field still cares for Cecilia and her children. We were glad to help them as we could, and the smile on their faces and their promise to keep praying for us is more than enough as a reward.

Be on the lookout. God will send people in need on your path.

Why God Sent a Surgeon to Subarina, Honduras on a Construction Team

I woke up hearing someone calling my name. I was taking a nap on the back seat of the bus as it slowly climbed the winding road leading to Subarina, Honduras. The bus had come to a stop, leaning to the right off the road. From my seat, I could see the steep valley on the left!

As I got out of the bus, I saw this young man lying on the road in front of the bus, his bicycle all banged up under the fender.

One look at him made me realize the seriousness of the situation. Large gaping wounds on his face, several teeth hanging on the broken jaw, deformed left thigh from a broken femur, and markedly swollen and deformed left arm. Back in the United States or any other developed nation, this patient with multiple trauma would be transported by EMT to a level-two trauma center. He was in danger of going into shock from bleeding and extreme pain from all the injuries. He could choke on his own blood that was profusely pouring into his mouth from the wounds around his mouth. He was still conscious and groaning. One glimmer of hope—he has no major head injury!

We were in Honduras on a construction mission. Fourteen of us went there on a one-week assignment to help construct a church building in this sparsely populated mountain village. After working there for a day, we had to take a break the next day due to a shortage of building supplies. We decided to take a trip to Yoro, the district headquarters, for some souvenir shopping and sightseeing. We spent several hours in Yoro, did some shopping, and were on our way back to Subarina.

The narrow two-way winding road up the mountain was hard for this old school bus with fourteen of us on board to climb. Fortunately, the traffic was not busy at all. The scenery was beautiful; deep green hills with tall trees all around. The weather was cool and pleasant. The only scary sight was the depth of the valley onto the left side of the road with no barriers to protect!

What am I doing on this construction mission in Honduras? A general surgeon by trade, with no experience in a construction job and not able to say a word of Spanish. When I heard about the mission trip, I put my name in. On the day before the trip, there was a meeting for the team at the church. Everyone was asked to write down on a piece of paper what he or she is most worried about on this trip. I remember writing down *the unexpected* and folding that paper and depositing it at the altar. Truly I was not worried about leaving my wife and children for a week and was least worried about the short flight. Going to a new culture and environment was exciting. Somehow, I was worried about *the unexpected*. Maybe this was it!

I asked the driver several questions in one breath: police, ambulance, 911, hospital, and many more. This was the worst place to be in an accident; no phone, no ambulance, no 911, and no hospital nearby. The nearest hospital was in Yoro where we came from, three hours by bus. The only transportation available is our school bus; and the construction team from the USA is the EMT, paramedic, as well as transport team!

We pulled out a seat from the bus on the road and laid the young man on it. We cut some tree limbs and used them as splints to immobilize his broken thigh and arm using towels and sheets we had. Thank God for the belt from our team leader; it was long enough to go around the patient and the seat! We lifted him up and placed him along the aisle at the back of the bus. Three of us from the team decided to go with him while the rest of the team walked the remaining three miles up the hill to Subarina.

I sat at the head end applying gentle pressure over his facial wounds. The local pastor who accompanied us was asked to ride with us as our interpreter. He was assigned to carry on a conversation with the patient to keep him from falling asleep and choking. But when he saw the gruesome and bloody face, the pastor closed his eyes and went on praying. Our attorney friend and team leader Glenn rose up to the occasion as my interpreter. Glenn did a fantastic job in instructing him to spit out or swallow the blood so that he won't choke on it. I wanted to keep him awake until we reached the hospital. Glenn could not believe what he was doing on that trip. He was a person who used to be deathly afraid of the sight of blood.

Later on, he narrated the story of his taking his son John to the emergency room and he himself getting hospitalized that day! Seeing the surgeon putting a stitch on John's head, Glenn fainted and fell on the floor at the hospital that day. When Glenn's wife called the ER to see how John was doing, she got to talk to the surgeon who said, "John is fine, but Glenn has to stay in hospital!"

Our eleven-member team was walking up the hill toward Subarina carrying the five-gallon water bottles and souvenir packages when a pickup truck with a cow on its bed stopped. The driver offered the team a ride on the back of the truck. Now there were eleven Americans surrounding a Honduran cow on the bed of that pickup truck that was climbing the hill. Obviously, this was a novel experience for the Americans as well as the Honduran cow. She lifted her tail and before anyone could say or do anything, did her number one and then number two. Everyone on the bed of that truck got a share of the gift from the "holy cow."

We reached Yoro at about 7:30 p.m. I was so glad to see a Honduran woman doctor in the emergency room. Holding my American College of Surgeons ID card, I approached her and introduced myself as a general surgeon from the USA and started talking about the injuries our patient had. In broken English, she informed me that all that they could do for our patient in Yoro was to put a better splint, give some pain medications, and send him to San Pedra Sulo to get surgical care. This main hospital for the district of Yoro did not have the ability to take care of major injuries from a road accident!

We were directed to report the accident to the office of the chief of police. We walked across the street to the office of the chief of police and there we listened to this tough police officer talking to us for several minutes in Spanish. Finally, our team leader Glenn turned around and gave us the summary. As follows, "As foreigners who got involved in a traffic accident in Honduras, I can detain you all for several days for questioning. Because you did the right thing in bringing the injured person to this hospital, and as your driver has agreed with me to transport the victim to the referral hospital in San Pedra Sulo tonight and bring back a receipt from the hospital by tomorrow, I am letting you all go free."

I was thinking, *Oh, he is not going to punish us for our good deed this time!*

As we walked back to the hospital, we saw the patient on the bed of a pickup truck with an IV line and ready to be driven off through the night. Thank God he reached the hospital over a hundred miles away, got operated on, and survived. When we returned to Subarina in the early morning hours, our team was still sitting there and praying for us.

Was there a reason for God to put a surgeon on a construction team in Subarina, Honduras? Yes, He had that young Honduran cyclist on His mind. Yes, He had to reveal the pathetic state of the health care system in the underdeveloped countries to the surgeon and challenge him for future medical mission trips.

How Much Do You Care?

Even stones have got stories to tell. In the book of Joshua, there is a reference to twelve stones that were picked by the Hebrew people from the bottom of River Jordan and set up on its bank on their long journey from slavery in Egypt to freedom in the land of Canaan. In Joshua 4:6–7 (NIV) it says:

> In the future, when your children ask you, 'What do these stones mean?' Tell them that the flow of the Jordan was cut off before the ark of the covenant of the Lord. When it crossed the Jordan, the waters of the Jordan were cut off. These stones are to be a memorial to the people of Israel forever.

It was customary for the Old Testament patriarchs to set up stones in places where they had visions or contacts with the angels of God. At times, they set the stones up as a memorial, at other times as a monument, and at times as a witness and reminder of the greatness and mercies of the Lord to the coming generations.

This is the first time for my wife and me to be in Zambia for a short medical mission under World Medical Mission. We had been to Kenya on three different occasions, and every time, it turned out to be a fulfilling and rewarding experience. Mukinge Mission Hospital in the Kesampe district of Zambia is about one hour and thirty minutes away by flight from Lusaka. This hospital caters to the medical needs of a large area of the country. With the limited resources and the meager manpower, they have been doing an excellent job for the past several decades.

Several voluntary missionaries from Europe and USA diligently serve here. Presently they have two missionary doctors from the US, one on a long term and another on a two-year commitment. A general surgeon from New Zealand has been serving at Mukinge Hospital for the past six years without taking a break! He is the only surgeon in this area! A young Zambian doctor has recently joined the medical staff. A CMO and another LMD also are on the staff to complete the medical staff roster.

As Dr. David Friend, the surgeon, was forced to take a three-month sabbatical and to go home, WWM was looking for surgery coverage for these three months. Paul Osteen from Houston, Texas agreed to serve for June and July, and I signed up for the month of August at Mukinge.

Newborns and children are all being cared for by the members of this wonderful medical team. They were excited to know that my pediatrician wife also will be accompanying me and is willing to serve during the same period. We sure did have some apprehension and concerns while considering this mission trip. Being in retirement for two years and staying away from the hospitals for this long period was one reason for concern. Health issues that go with age was another. Safety issues in Africa were yet another. It was just recently only our daughter and her young family had to cancel their plans to serve and return home from Tanzania due to safety issues there.

Dr. Paul Osteen was the first name that came to mind for us to talk about these and other issues. His input was of immense help in making up our minds for the mission trip to Mukinge Hospital, Zambia. Paul was another godsent person in our life in retirement. On the very first trip to Tenwek Hospital, Kenya, my bag with every last piece of my clothing for our stay there did not arrive at Nairobi on the same flight with us. We were told that the bag will be sent to the hospital the next day. Paul, who's already serving at Tenwek and who knew very well that "the next day" for the Kenyan Airlines people could be after several "next days," decided to present me with two plastic bags, one with a pair of sneakers and the other with all the essential clothes for me to survive and work for the next few days!

He was there to guide me and help me through the routines in the Department of Surgery as well. I was quite apprehensive about the cases that are out of my *comfort zone*, and sure enough, they had many. Head trauma was very common in that referral hospital where neurosurgery was handled by the surgeon on call. Pediatric and neonatal surgery, too, was another major field where I felt uncomfortable. In most mission hospitals, the physician will have to do the best he/ she can, as there was no other option! Paul was there to guide me through my initial cases.

Paul Osteen, a board-certified general surgeon with vascular surgery training, had been in private practice in Arkansas when his father Pastor John Osteen passed away. Paul gave up his practice and moved to Houston, Texas to help his younger brother to take care of their dad's church. They sure did take care of that church in Houston which received the abundant blessings from the Lord and grew into the present Lakewood Church in downtown Houston at the former Astro Stadium, attracting tens of thousands of believers for every service, and Joel's television ministry and written messages reaching millions around the world.

Paul is an associate pastor at the Lakewood Church where he directs the missions. He continues to spend six months every year helping surgeons at mission hospitals in Africa, Haiti, South America, and Central America. His wife Jennifer and their children have accompanied Paul in most of his mission fields. My wife and I had the privilege to get to know this man of God and his beautiful family at Tenwek Hospital, Kenya. Paul is an unassuming, soft-spoken person and wears a constant smile on his face. He is an accomplished surgeon who taught himself to become a special surgeon for African mission fields. He is a great Bible teacher, too, who preaches through his actions and uses words when necessary.

It was by divine providence that Paul happened to be there at Tenwek Hospital all the three times we were there. Our second term in Kenya was for two months and that was a very rewarding and fulfilling experience. Paul has a special gift of finding the needy and taking care of the one in most need in a discrete way. Many are the patients who received financial help from Paul without much publicity or fanfare. His mission is always one on one. Counseling and praying with the one in distress are special gifts for this servant of God.

The third time that I was at Tenwek for a two-week mission tour, I got sick the very day I reached there. I could do very little work, and I became a burden rather than a help for Paul whom I came there to help by sharing surgery calls. He was very understanding, considerate, and helpful to me. He took my calls and helped me at the time of my illness. His final diagnosis on my condition was that I was suffering from separation anxiety, as this time for the first time ever, I traveled alone. And the prescription: "Never travel abroad without your wife Leya with you."

Paul is a hardworking man who is not afraid of challenges; at the same time, he is such a humble person who will always make others feel more important than himself. No wonder he has a huge number of good friends all across the globe!

At Mukinge, we were following the Osteens who just left after serving for two months. We were staying in the same house that the Osteens stayed. Paul had made a special request for the housing authorities to allot the same house for us. This was a house the Osteens had invested a lot of their personal funds for renovation. They decided to stock the food pantry and the closets with most of the things we would ever need for our short stay there. The whole house was repainted and new curtains were installed. New bath towels and sheets were placed. Thanks to the Osteens, we had such a luxury in a remote part of Zambia for a mission house! Paul had already bragged to the other missionaries on the campus about the cooking skills of Leya. He also mentioned our health concerns and our age concerns too. It sure made a difference. They seemed to know a lot about us before we arrived, and they sure treated us well.

You may be wondering why I started this article writing about those stones from the bottom of River Jordan mentioned in the book of Joshua. We, too, are seeing a set of stones near to our housing at Mukinge. One large stone and two smaller ones as markers on our path to the hospital. These stones were placed there by Paul for a special purpose, we were told. The largest stone is close to a hook over the metal lid covering a large manhole, and the other stones mark the shallow ditches and dips in the path that is covered with grass. Paul set them there so that we, his friends, will not stumble and fall when we make our way to the hospital and back, especially at night. To us, this is the ultimate in caring for the well-being of your friends.

There was a fireplace in the house where we were staying. Before leaving the house, the Osteens made sure that there was enough firewood stocked inside the fireplace for the Mathews to use. This obviously is not the firewood that we are used to buying in the stores; they are handpicked from the field, and it makes it doubly special. They walked that extra mile to make sure that every need of their friends was addressed and attended to. What an example of true friendship!

For us, the stones on our daily path to the Mukinge Hospital represent the love and care from true friends. They cared enough to think of the safety and convenience in detail and did something about it.

How far do you and I go in caring for others?

Out of your comfort zone.

You Are Never Too Old to Learn

Our plan into retirement was to go to medically underserved areas in the world and use our expertise to benefit the needy. Little did we know that each day, we are going to learn something new! We chose Tenwek Hospital, Bomet, Kenya as our place of service for the first time after retirement. This large mission hospital is located about two and a half hours drive from Nairobi. Bomet is a beautiful town about six thousand feet above mean sea level. With the temperate climate and plenty of rain, the whole area is always green.

Most of the doctors here are volunteering their service. Most of them are from the US and are long-term missionaries. They spend six months to a year in the US after serving here for three years at a stretch. They utilize that time for sharpening their skills in their respective fields as well as talking to church and groups to raise funds for sustaining them at Tenwek. Their zeal for this place is great, and they are all dedicating their life to this underserved region of Africa.

I was on call for surgery this past weekend from Saturday, 8:00 a.m. to Monday, 8:00 a.m. One surgery resident and a medical student are on call with you in surgery. We made rounds in the morning on all surgical patients. By the time we were finished with the rounds, there were two calls from the casualty department. A two-year-old boy was brought to the hospital with difficulty in breathing and cough after choking on an orange seed.

Another four-year-old boy who had a ventriculoperitoneal shunt since early infancy for congenital hydrocephalus was brought in by his parents. He was having severe headaches and visual disturbances for the past couple of weeks due to a nonfunctioning VP shunt. Our resident in surgery, Agneta, immediately did a ventricular tap and got clear CSF under high pressure. The next step is to replace the malfunctioning shunt, and she scheduled the child for that.

Of course, the child with the orange seed in his air passage should be taken care of first. We took the child to the theater and under general anesthesia administered by a nurse anesthetist, Agneta proceeded with rigid bronchoscopy and got the seed from his left main bronchus and saved the little boy from suffocating.

Then it was the boy with the malfunctioning VP shunt who had his turn in surgery. Our Kenyan surgery resident was so confident and knowledgeable. She moved like a neurosurgeon and proceeded with the surgery on that four-year-old boy and replaced the malfunctioning shunt with a new one. Two procedures, both out of my comfort zone and both not attempted by general surgeons in the USA. That morning, I watched with amazement the ease with which a Kenyan surgery resident did both procedures. A really humbling and learning experience.

Before we were finished with the second case, there was another call from the casualty department. This time it was a man who was assaulted a few days ago with an axe over his head. He was taken to a local hospital where after taking an X-ray of his skull, they put a few sutures on the scalp and kept him for observation. Today he was not able to speak well, and they decided to send him to our facility. This young man was still conscious and alert but had difficulty in carrying on a conversation. He had a large area of depressed fracture over the left side of his head. He needed to go to surgery to explore the scalp wound, a good washout, and elevation of his skull fracture.

Under general anesthesia, his scalp was incised and skull exposed. A large area of the markedly depressed and fragmented skull was exposed; the fragments were elevated, a tear in the outer covering of the brain was repaired, blood clots from the top of the dura were washed out, and the scalp wounds were repaired. By the time the patient was sent to the intensive care unit, it was ten at night and I retired to the apartment for a little rest. That night was uneventful, and I was able to get a few hours of rest.

Sunday morning, we took rounds after the church service. The interns and the resident had made their rounds earlier in the morning. All our patients from Saturday were doing fairly well. After the rounds, I returned to my apartment and rested for a little while. Little did I know what was waiting in the wings for the rest of Sunday.

That evening, a nine-month-old baby boy was sent to our casualty department with *rectal prolapse* for over a week! This poor baby was kept in a local hospital for several days with his condition deteriorating daily until today when they decided to send him on our way. He was critically ill with a segment of his dead small bowel protruding through the anal orifice. What the local doctor thought was prolapse was intussusception indeed, and the baby was on the verge of death. His only chance of getting any better was surgical removal of the dead bowel, and that sure carried a very high risk. We took the baby to surgery that night after heroic efforts to correct the electrolyte imbalance and severe dehydration. The baby made it through surgery but succumbed the second postoperative day.

The same afternoon we had another three-month-old baby sent to the casualty. She already had three abdominal surgeries in the span of two weeks, and she was leaking stool from her abdominal incision. Apparently, this unfortunate baby had her first surgery for a hernia necessitating resection anastomosis of a segment of the small bowel resulting in leakage of stool. Two more surgeries followed, and at both times, more injuries were inflicted on her small bowel. Poor girl had a long transverse incision on her abdomen with stool oozing out from it. A drain in the lower abdomen had nothing coming out from it! This girl was kept in our ICU for another day before making the trip to the theater for another exploration.

At surgery, two areas of the anastomosis with breakdown and leaking and four leaking enterotomies were encountered in a twenty-five-centimeter segment of her small bowel. This segment was resected, and the ends of the bowel were brought out as ileostomy and mucus fistula. She is doing well and is getting ready for reconnection of her bowel during her next trip to the operation theater.

That Sunday evening, we received two more victims of violence. A young lady was viciously attacked by her sister-in-law, who inflicted two deep, gaping wounds on the right side of her head and face with a *panga*. The wound over the head had gone deep to produce a clean, deep cut on the skull for about five inches long.

A twenty-four-year-old man was attacked and chopped down by his neighbor also using a *panga*. He had several deep cuts over his skull with multiple open fractures and brain tissue oozing out of the wounds! A deep cut over his back had cut part of his shoulder blade! Wound over his right knee had cut the kneecap into two clean pieces. A large slash across his lower back had slashed his paravertebral muscles and nicked the spines.

One after another, both of these were taken to surgery and were taken care of. By the time both of them were out of the theater, it was four thirty in the morning! It was worth the effort; both of them are doing well and are out of the intensive care unit!

Blessing from unexpected sources.

Acknowledgments

Surgeon on Trial came to fruition only because of the support and encouragement from many.

On top of the list is my dear wife and life partner, Leya. Through the past fifty years of our marriage, she stood with me in every experience. Going through the medical lability issues do take a toll on the spouse. A spouse who understands and stands with you is the keystone for your success. Leya has been my strongest support through each stage of the trial. She was on my side listening to each word that was uttered in the trial and watching the body language of the attorneys, jurors, and the presiding judge. Her wise counsel and fervent prayer are my strongholds. Thanks for still being there!

The support and encouragement from my readers gave me the courage to venture out with this book—my third publication. Your comments and words of encouragement in person and via social media were of much help. Thanks for your continued support.

My patients, you are the whole reason for this venture. Medical profession is a noble one, and I enjoyed each day in practice. I am humbled by the trust and confidence that you placed in me. It is an enormous undertaking that each one of you did: trusting another human being and letting him put you to sleep and operate on you! How much more vulnerable one can be! I value your trust, and I thank you from the bottom of my heart. Best result for the patient is every surgeon's dream. Unfortunately, no surgeon can guarantee perfect results all the time. Thanks for accepting me as I am with the warts and all and for taking time to read the *Surgeon on Trial.*

Dr. Theodosius Mar Thoma Metropolitan, the spiritual head of the worldwide Mar Thoma Church gave me the inspiration to publish our experiences on the International Medical Mission trips. My sincere thanks to the metropolitan for the encouragement and blessings.

About the Author

K. E. Mathew has retired from practicing general surgery and settled in South Louisiana. With his wife Leya, a pediatrician, they have made several medical mission trips to Africa and Mexico. They have three daughters and four grandchildren.

His hobbies include travel, photography, gardening, and small group Bible studies.

Dr. Mathew has authored two other books, *I Don't Want My Mom to Pray for Me* and *Orphans of Mundakapadam*. These are available on Amazon.

CPSIA information can be obtained
at www.ICGtesting.com
Printed in the USA
BVHW041341011222
653207BV00003B/13

9 798885 401616